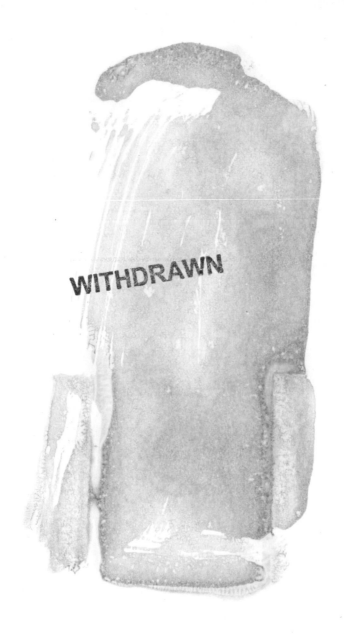

How To Know

THE CACTI

Pictured Keys for determining the native cacti of the United States and many of the introduced species.

E. YALE DAWSON

WM. C. BROWN COMPANY PUBLISHERS
135 SOUTH LOCUST STREET • DUBUQUE, IOWA 52003

THE PICTURED-KEY NATURE SERIES

"How to Know the Insects," Jaques, 1947

"Living Things—How to Know Them," Jaques, 1946

"How to Know the Trees," Jaques, 1946

"Plant Families—How to Know Them," Jaques, 1948

"How to Know the Economic Plants," Jaques, 1948, 1958

"How to Know the Spring Flowers," Cuthbert, 1943, 1949

"How to Know the Mosses and Liverworts," Conard, 1944, 1956

"How to Know the Land Birds," Jaques, 1947

"How to Know the Fall Flowers," Cuthbert, 1948

"How to Know the Immature Insects," Chu, 1949

"How to Know the Protozoa," Jahn, 1949

"How to Know the Mammals," Booth, 1949

"How to Know the Beetles," Jaques, 1951

"How to Know the Spiders," Kaston, 1952

"How to Know the Grasses," Pohl, 1953

"How to Know the Fresh-Water Algae," Prescott, 1954

"How to Know the Western Trees," Baerg, 1955

"How to Know the Seaweeds," Dawson, 1956

"How to Know the Freshwater Fishes," Eddy, 1957

"How to Know the Weeds," Jaques, 1959

"How to Know the Water Birds," Jaques-Ollivier, 1960

"How to Know the Butterflies," Ehrlich, 1961

"How to Know the Eastern Land Snails," Burch, 1962

"How to Know the Grasshoppers," Helfer, 1963

"How to Know the Cacti," Dawson, 1963

Other Subjects in Preparation

Printed in U.S.A.

FOREWORD

THE CACTI of the United States, with the exception of the relatively few species growing east of the Mississippi River, were largely brought into scientific knowledge during the decade prior to the Civil War. At that time several great expeditions for the Pacific Railroad, the U.S. and Mexican Boundary Survey, and the Gadsden Purchase, opened up the southwestern regions for botanical investigation. Most of the work on the cacti was done by a single man, Dr. George Engelmann, a physician of St. Louis, Missouri. Although he was able to devote only his residual hours to botanical study he succeeded in publishing during a few years a great volume of scholarly works, especially on desert plants. Perhaps the finest engraved illustrations of cacti ever prepared were published in his reports, and I take great pleasure in presenting reproductions of some of them in the present book.

Following Engelmann's work there was a lapse of half a century in the critical study of American cacti, but in 1919 the Carnegie Institution of Washington began the publication of a four-volume monograph of the cacti of the world, representing the culmination of many years of pioneer investigations by Nathaniel Lord Britton of the New York Botanical Garden and J. N. Rose of the U. S. National Museum. This monumental work immediately became the Bible of cactophiles, and a desideratum for book collectors because of its magnificent colored plates, mostly by Mary Eaton. It soon was out of print and is now obtainable only at great price. In 1937 Scott Haselton, editor for the Cactus and Succulent Society of America, reprinted those volumes (with black-and-white plates), but these too have become high priced and in short supply.

Other than the Britton and Rose monograph there have been many small books treating cactus floras of particular states, or of cacti in general for the amateur gardener, but there has not appeared any handbook of the cacti of the United States designed to provide a ready means of identifying the commoner species that one encounters in the field and in everyday cultivation. To fill such a lack, this little book was prepared.

Several individuals have been most helpful in making possible the presentation of the illustrations. Each of them I wish to thank.

Through the cooperation of Mrs. G. Philip Bauer of the Carnegie Institution of Washington and Dr. Jason Swallen of the Smithsonian Institution, the original paintings prepared by Mary Eaton for *The Cactaceae* were made available, and a number of them are reproduced here.

iii

Mr. Don Ollis of Santa Barbara made photo-reproductions of the engravings from the works of George Engelmann and the Mary Eaton paintings, and also provided other photographs.

Several others were helpful in providing photographs, especially Mr. W. H. Earle of the Desert Botanical Garden of Arizona, Mr. Harry Johnson of Johnson Cactus Gardens, Paramount, Calif., Mr. and Mrs. Don Skinner of Los Angeles, Dr. Robert Craig, of Baldwin Park, Calif., and Mr. Edward S. Taylor of Los Angeles.

The classification in this manual follows that proposed by Britton and Rose, and quite generally accepted by cactus students in the country. Several changes in name (mostly from species to varietal status) have been adopted in accord with the recent studies by Dr. Lyman Benson of Pomona College, California, who is currently preparing a monograph of the cacti of the United States.

Santa Ynez, California
July 1961

E. YALE DAWSON

The cacti have many peculiar characters which make them different from other plants and add to their interest. They are so adept at withstanding abuse that caring for them is very simple. They constitute the predominating vegetation in many desert areas and are widely raised in gardens and greenhouses.

Lovers of these plants will find Dr. Dawson's manual the book they have looked for.

Editor

CONTENTS

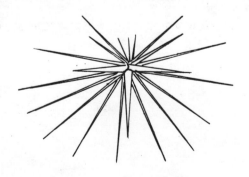

The writer examines the fruit af *la tuna*, a cactus long cultivated for food by Spanish missionaries and ranchers along *El Camino Real* in California.

CACTI OF THE WESTERN WORLD

EITHER classical Greek nor Latin had a word for them! Indeed, no one in the civilized world had ever seen a cactus until Columbus' party stepped ashore on Hispaniola. Like corn, tobacco and tomatoes, this prominent group of plants we call cacti was confined to the American continents and had carried out its extraordinary speciation unconnected with the floras of the rest of the world.

Early botanists, in searching the ancient languages for a name to apply to the strange plants, used the Greek word for thistle which seemed the nearest approach to such spiny vegetables. Ever since, we have known them as *cactus*.

No soooner had the early explorers of the New World oriented themselves to the wonders and novelties of the West Indies than they began to carry home these curious succulent plants that so readily survived long sea voyages without water or attention. Soon the greenhouses of Europe were stocked with them, and along the Mediterranean coasts, especially of Spain, Italy and North Africa, many were found to thrive in outdoor gardens.

In time some of the common and tolerant species found their ways to semi-arid regions of many parts of the world, and became established as naturalized plants where they have often become major pests. In Australia, for example, introduced prickly pears grew so well and spread so widely that until controls were developed there were many thousands of square miles overgrown by their thorny thickets.

Today one finds cacti growing "wild" in arid situations in many parts of the old world, and our modern motion pictures filmed on location in the Mediterranean region often show the anachronism of a cactus plant within a scene portraying an ancient time at which they were unknown.

Such errors in film editing are seldom noticed, however, for few people are aware either of the restricted geographic origin of the cacti or of the ways in which the cacti differ from various other kinds of succulent, spiny, desert plants. Thus, such plants more closely related to lillies and orchids as century plants (Fig. 1), yuccas, joshua trees (Fig. 2), and the like are often erroneously considered cacti by the layman. The spiny ocotillo of our southwestern deserts (Fig. 3) is understandably mistaken, and among cultivated, spiny succulents a host of African species of *Euphorbia* (Fig. 4) are confused with cacti by the uninitiated.

1

Figure 1. A Century Plant *(Agave)* in flower. This is an American desert plant of the Amarillis family and not related to the cacti.

Figure 2. The Joshua Tree *(Yucca brevifolia)*, a spiny leaved desert plant of California belonging to the Lily family and not related to the cacti.

Figure 3. The Ocotillo, or Jacob's Staff (*Fouquieria splendens*), a spiny stemmed desert plant of the Southwest belonging to a family of its own and unrelated to the cacti.

Figure 4. *Euphorbia valida*, one of many succulent members of this genus in Africa. These plants produce various kinds of spines and have fleshy forms closely resembling cacti in many ways. They occupy desert regions of the old world as counterparts of the American cacti.

HOW TO RECOGNIZE THE CACTI

ET us see by what means we may recognize the cactus from among other succulent or spiny plants. To do so one must be aware of the extraordinary diversity of form and habitat found in this plant family.

First we may dispell the misconception that cacti grow only in desert regions. The fact is, one may find cacti growing under a great variety of climatic conditions from the very dry to the very wet, and although the succulent habit is the rule, some species form woody thorn bushes or trees. Notwithstanding extreme diversity of form and habit, all have in common a special structure known as the areole.

The areole is the remarkable growth center in the cactus,—a specialized kind of bud. The areoles form little spots on the stems from which the spines, wool and bristles arise, and these localities also produce the branches and flowers. They are usually easily recognized because of the spines they bear, but are, on this account, extremely variable. In some they consist only of a little pad of fine felt or wool, but usually have one or more distinct spines. Sometimes there are very tiny, short spines called glochids, and again there may be long hairs or bristles (see Figs. 15, 17, 19, 22).

Some cacti, such as *Pereskia* and *Opuntia* in our flora have leaves (broad and persistent in *Pereskia;* small, awl-shaped in *Opuntia* (Fig. 5), and it is in the axil of these leaves that the areoles occur, just as a bud occurs in the axil of a leaf of any ordinary shrubby plant. All the other cacti in our flora lack leaves, but show by the areoles the place where the leaves of the ancestral type may have been.

Since most cacti either lack leaves, or the leaves are small and ephemeral, the stem takes over the function of the leaves, not only in

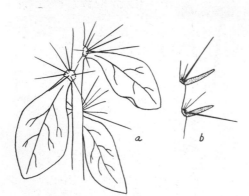

Figure 5. Two kinds of cactus leaves: a, broad, veined leaves of *Pereskia;* b, awl-shaped, deciduous leaves of *Opuntia*. The spine clusters and leaves arise from areoles on the stems.

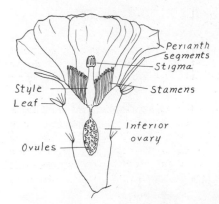

Perianth
segments
Stigma
Style
Stamens
Leaf
Inferior
ovary
Ovules

Figure 6. Generalized longitudinal section of a typical cactus flower *(Opuntia)* showing relationship of parts.

food manufacture, but in food and water storage. Consequently, we find a great diversity of stem form among these fleshy plants in which adaptation to periods of drought or to habitats with limited water supply have created of the stems various shapes of water-storage vessels. In all of our cacti except the leafy *Pereskia, the* stems are succulent and store greater or lesser amounts of water. In some, however, the stems store little water compared to the roots which may be extraordinarily enlarged and modified for this purpose.

The flowers of the cacti are of far more uniform structure than the stems, but are, nevertheless, variable in size, shape and origin. They are all perfect flowers, with inferior ovary, indefinite numbers of perianth segments with little distinction between petals and sepals, numerous stamens, and a single style with several stigma lobes (Fig. 6). These floral characteristics, when taken in conjunction with the usual vegetative features of the cacti, namely, the succulent stems, the absence of flattened or persistent leaves, and the spine-bearing areoles, provide a ready means of recognizing most of the members of this family as distinct from other succulent or spiny plants.

GEOGRAPHIC DISTRIBUTION

DESPITE the fact that the cactus family evolved in the American continents and remained essentially confined to them, the remarkable adaptability of these plants has permitted them to spread into a great variety of habitats in almost all parts of the New World. Thus, we find in tropical forests numbers of cacti growing epiphytically with orchids and bromeliads on the trees (Fig. 7), others climbing up from the forest floor with vines and lianas (Fig. 8), and here and there in a clearing or thicket a columnar or candelabra-like

5

Figure 7. A forest tree in the West Indies completely covered with epiphytic *Hylocereus*.

Figure 8. A clambering cactus *(Harrisia)* coming up through a tropical vine thicket in Cuba.

form. Along the seashore of Caribbean islands, on limestone rocks wet with salt spray are the melocacti (Fig. 9). In the hot deserts of the southwestern United States, Mexico, Chile and Argentina are a profusion of cacti, but also one finds them on the snowy slopes of high mountains, from 10,000 to 16,000 feet in Peru, Bolivia, Mexico and California. So well do some species tolerate extremes of heat and cold that they are found widely over the great plains of the central United States and Canada. The remarkably diverse habitats of the cacti in the U.S. and the extensive range throughout a majority of our states are, indeed, major reasons for the preparation of this book, which, on these accounts, has a far wider application and use than would be provided by a manual on the cacti of the southwestern deserts alone.

The greatest numbers and varieties of cacti occur in Mexico, and the center of distribution and evolution of the group seems to have been in the Mexico-Caribbean island region. From there they have spread north into North America as far as central Canada, and south into South America to Patagonia and the Galapagos Islands. Many of the evolving lines became isolated in these opposite continental areas and developed into genera that are now confined only to one continent or the other. Others apparently have spread back and forth between the continents and are now widespread in both.

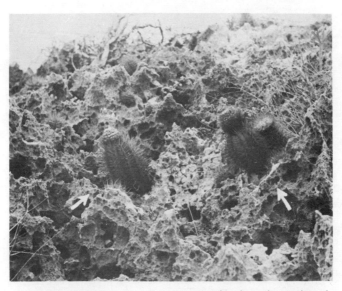

Figure 9. Eroded, cavernous limestone rocks along the seashore in Cuba with cephalium-bearing plants of the genus *Cactus* growing in the soilless cavities.

7

In the process of evolution and speciation many of the connecting lines between groups have disappeared so that some of the genera of cacti are exceedingly distinct and contain only a few strongly marked and readily identified relic species. In the West Indies, for example, the genus *Leptocereus* seems to be an ancient one that now is nearly extinct (Fig. 10). Only a few species remain in Cuba and Puerto Rico, and some of these are represented in nature by only tiny colonies of a few plants that have survived to our day. On the other hand, there are other groups of cacti, notably *Opuntia*, *Mammillaria* and *Echinocereus* that are evolving rapidly today and are still spreading out into new habitats through the adaptability of new mutants to changing environments. In such "plastic" groups as these there are large numbers of "species," many of them closely related and distinguishable with difficulty. Taxonomic treatment of these has varied depending upon the specialist's recognition of certain morphological characters that he may consider of specific value. Accordingly, although in this book we have attempted to abide by some of the most recent treatments by well-recognized authors, the names used will not always agree with those found in other handbooks, and one may wish to refer to listings of synonyms to find equivalents.

Before leaving the subject of geographic distribution we should make brief mention of the place of a number of cacti as the dominant

Figure 10. Perhaps the rarest cactus in the world, *Leptocereus leonii* grows on a limestone cliff in Cuba. The species is nearly extinct, only about half a dozen plants remaining alive in nature.

member of a plant association and a biological community. Thus, we have the Giant Saguaro of Arizona (Fig. 11), so prominent and abundant a species that it constitutes the principal element in a plant association that supports a unique and especially remarkable biota. The story of this wonderful community has been presented most beautifully by Paul G. Howes in his 1954 book, The Giant Cactus Forest and its World. There are many similar cactus communities in many parts of the New World, but none so well documented. All of these, from the *Machaerocereus* thickets of Baja California to the *Trichocereus* forests of the Andes, await the critical studies of naturalists who can interpret the complexities of plant and animal life associations.

Figure 11. The Giant Cactus, or Saguaro, of southern Arizona, our largest cactus and one for which a National Monument has been established.

THE STUDY OF CACTI

PERHAPS the greatest stimulus to the study of cacti by amateurs came some forty years ago with the publication of the monumental four-volume work by Britton and Rose on the cacti of the world. Not long after that a society was formed in Pasadena, California, which has become of national proportions with a number of affiliated local societies and a regular biennial National Convention. This, the Cactus and Succulent Society of America publishes the "Journal" which is the principal medium for the issuing of both scientific and popular papers on cacti in the United States. The "Journal" has published a great deal of information on the U.S. cacti during the past 32 years, and its editor, Scott Haselton, has been instrumental in organizing and publishing a number of special books on the subject. (See reference list page 20.) Although several local state cactus floras have appeared for California, Arizona, Texas, Colorado, etc., there has not yet been a treatment of the cacti of the United States as a whole. An authoritative monograph is now in preparation by Dr. Lyman Benson of Pomona College, and we may look forward to having this thoroughgoing reference in a few years.

Interest on the part of amateurs in cacti has stemmed not only from their curious form and unusual flowers, but from the ease with which many of them can be grown. Their resistance to drought serves the

Figure 12. *Epiphyllum anguliger*, one of the popular forms of the tropical "orchid cacti."

householder well who frequently forgets to water his plants. Further, the ease with which potted specimens can be moved in and out with the seasons has made them popular in climates to which they would seem ill adapted, such as England and Japan. Thus, one of the most successfully grown collections of South American cacti in my experience was in Hamburg, Germany, where all the plants were stored each winter on kitchen and basement shelves. In the spring they were put out in the glasshouse, given good watering with liquid fertilizer and brought quickly into glorious flower.

Because of the great variety of habitats, soils and conditions of moisture and temperature to which cacti are adapted, methods of cultivation may often vary, and one should consult a handbook of cultivation of which there are several for instructions not only on soils, light, fertilizer, water, etc., but on methods of grafting by which many are most successfully grown (see references). Greenhouse culture of many tropical species for their unusual vegetative form and flowers has become a hobby for many from Canada to New Zealand. The hybridization of some kinds, particularly the so-called "orchid cacti" (*Epiphyllum* spp.) (Fig. 12) has also become a prominent field of cactus culture and will be of interest to the student.

PREPARATION OF SPECIMENS

 LTHOUGH the cultivation of cacti as a hobby holds many satisfactions, and, when done under favorable conditions can provide for an excellent technical understanding of the plants, the scientific study of wild kinds must be accompanied by herbarium specimens to provide permanent records of the actual plants as they occur in nature. The relative difficulty of making herbarium specimens of cacti, as compared to most flowering plants, has, perhaps, been the principal deterrant to their study, for most botanists in the field cannot take time to process the bulky, spiny, succulent plants, and do not include them in their collections.

Since good field collections of cacti are still sparse in herbaria of this country, a few notes on their preparation may encourage users of this book to make good permanent specimens to aid us in obtaining a more accurate knowledge of these plants in the United States.

A good herbarium specimen should contain not only critical parts of the plant, but a habit photograph to augment the dried parts, together with ample field data on the label. Just as a single twig or leaf of a flowering plant provides poor material as a specimen, so likewise with the cactus. The herbarium material should include flower and fruit as well as stem and root parts (Fig.. 13).

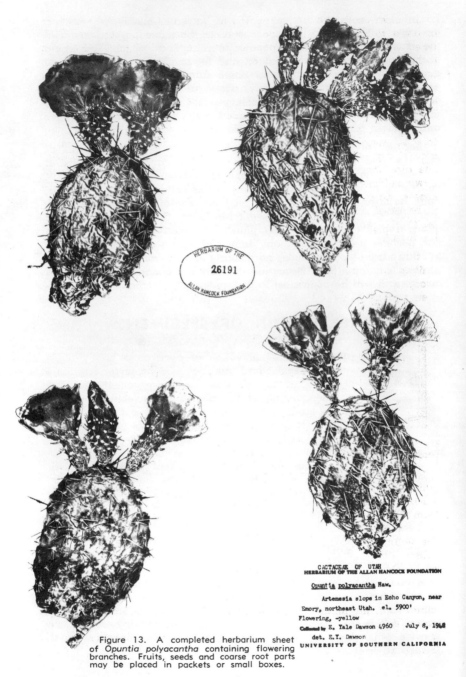

Figure 13. A completed herbarium sheet of *Opuntia polyacantha* containing flowering branches. Fruits, seeds and coarse root parts may be placed in packets or small boxes.

CACTACEÆ OF UTAH
HERBARIUM OF THE ALLAN HANCOCK FOUNDATION

Opuntia polyacantha Haw.

Artemesia slope in Echo Canyon, near Emory, northeast Utah. el. 5900'
Flowering, -yellow
Collected by E. Yale Dawson 4960   July 6, 1948
det. E.Y. Dawson
UNIVERSITY OF SOUTHERN CALIFORNIA

In most cases the fleshy parts will have to be split or sectioned in order to reduce the succulent bulk to pressable proportions. Flattened stems can be split lengthwise while cylindrical ones may need to be prepared as split halves as well as cross sections to show the important characteristics. Excess flesh may be scooped out with a spoon, and the remaining fleshy surface sprinkled with salt that will soon cause water to be exuded to such an extent that it may actually be *poured* off. If such split, sectioned and salted specimens are put in a regular plant press and the drying felts changed at frequent intervals, suitable record specimens can easily be prepared. Spines, of course, may often be bothersome, especially those that project in various directions, but with a little practice, even those may be pressed down sufficiently to permit the dry material to be tied to herbarium sheets. Some material may be so three-dimensional that it may need to be dried for housing in herbarium boxes, and this may especially be true of some spiny fruits that cannot satisfactorily be preserved by pressing.

Since cacti in the field may not always be found in flowering and fruiting condition, one may often cultivate the plant for some time to produce the missing parts, whereupon the complete herbarium specimen can be prepared from the greenhouse or garden.

MORPHOLOGY OF CACTI

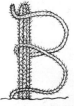 EFORE the student undertakes to use the following key he needs to acquire a fundamental knowledge of the general morphology of the cacti, the major variations in the form and structure of parts, and the principal terms that will appear in the key later on. Accordingly, a number of diagrams are presented here in succession and for ready reference.

Inasmuch as the stems of cacti have taken over from the leaves, which are essentially absent, the function of food manufacture, and since the needs of water storage have often greatly modified their form, the stems are usually the most conspicuous parts of the plant and the first to be considered in a morphological analysis. Even in the youngest seedlings the swollen, fleshy character of the stem is evident, and as growth proceeds a definite form is established in which the stem remains a simple unbranched, more or less spherical or columnar body, or produces branches of various kinds, either jointed or unjointed (Fig. 14). Some of the species of *Ferocactus* are representative of the unbranched form with maximum storage capacity compared to surface area, while some of the flattened *Opuntia* species show a maximum degree of branching and leaf-like flattening of the jointed stems.

Figure 14. Various stem forms of cacti, both jointed and un-jointed.

Although in some opuntias the spine-bearing areoles may be borne on the surface with little or no elevation or modification, in most instances the spines occur on ribs or tubercles (Fig. 15). A majority of erect, columnar or clambering "cereoid" cacti have ribbed stems, sometimes with definite numbers of ribs. In many of the cylindrical opuntias ribs are scarcely evident, but the low, often spirally offset elevations bearing the spines constitute a minimum development of tubercles. In the genera *Coryphantha* and *Mammillaria*, however, the stem is exceedingly shortened and the spine-bearing elevations elongated to form nipple-like tubercles with the spine clusters at their apices.

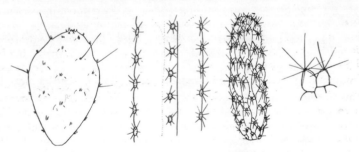

Figure 15. Some examples of areole position, left to right: superficial, *Opuntia*; elevated on ribs, *Cereus*; on low tubercles, *Opuntia prolifera*; terminal on nipple-like tubercles, *Mammillaria*.

A few other features of the stem may be used in identification, such as the color of the waxy, waterproof epidermal layer of the plant, the presence or absence of a powdery bloom, on the surface texture, whether smooth and shiny or provided with a soft epidermal velvet.

Although the stems of cacti are almost always the principal water storage organs serviced by slender, shallow, spreading, fibrous roots capable of picking up moisture in minimum time, this is not always true (Fig. 16). In our flora we have several examples of cacti in which the roots partially, or almost wholly, take over the water storage function with remarkable modification. In several opuntias the roots are fleshy and tend to take over the storage function only seasonally

Figure 16. Some examples of fibrous and fleshy root systems.

when the above-ground portions may be subject to freezing. Sometimes, too, a small *Opuntia* plant may have an enormously extended root system 20-50 times its volume lying a few inches below the ground surface. However, the especially modified storage roots are found in *Peniocereus* and *Wilcoxia*. In the former there are enormous "tubers" weighing up to 50 pounds bearing spindly stems of a few ounces. *Wilcoxia* produces a group of 2-3 dozen "tubers" resembling sweet potatoes and an above-ground stem only ¼ inch in diameter.

Despite these exceptions, one notes in general that it is the fleshy, succulent stem of cacti, storing so important a substance as water in arid regions, that has been the subject of a double evolution in which the water storage capacity has been matched by another character of survival value, namely the development of an armament of spines serving to discourage penetration by vegetarian animals. These spines are of a great many kinds, as already intimated, from little more than soft hairs to bristles, needle-like spines and heavy hooks, and we have seen that the spines are borne in areoles (Fig. 17) distributed over the plant body in various manners. In some they are scattered over flat, pad-like stem segments; they may form rows or ribbed columns, or they may form a tight spiral around a cylindrical joint, more or less elevated on tubercles. The form, number, color, position, etc. of spines provide useful characters in identifying cacti, and many of these will be noted in the key to follow. Some of the principal kinds of spines should be recognized.

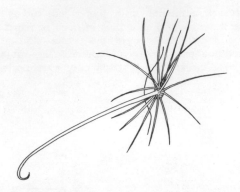

Figure 17. An areole bearing spines of two kinds: several curved, acicular *radial* spines, and a single hooked *central* spine.

Apart from wool, hair and fine bristles that will easily be recognized coming from the areoles of such plants as *Cephalocereus, Mammillaria* and *Lophocereus* there are several distinctive kinds and shapes of spines. Spines may be straight, slender-conical, subulate, or acicular (Fig. 18), or they may be more or less curved or hooked. They may be smooth or cross-ribbed, and they may be needle-sharp or microscopically barbed. In *Opuntia* we find some of the most remarkable spine developments, for in this group is found a special kind of minute, barbed spine called the *glochid* (Fig. 19) which may occur in great numbers in the areoles of such species as *Opuntia basilaris*. Among the cylindrical opuntias, most of the North American species have

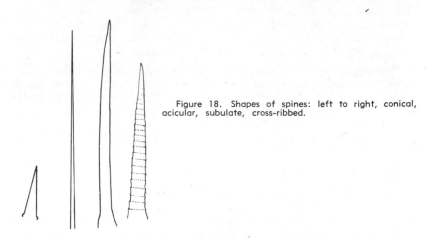

Figure 18. Shapes of spines: left to right, conical, acicular, subulate, cross-ribbed.

slender, straight, barbed spines enclosed by a remarkably fine, papery sheath, (see *Opuntia davisii*, Fig. 31) while those closely related in South America lack such sheaths.

16

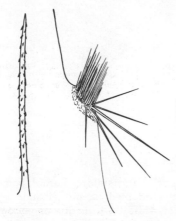

Figure 19. An areole bearing several acicular spines and a tuft of glochids. A single glochid, much magnified, is shown on the left with its minute retuse barbs.

Despite the uniformity of floral characters pointed out above, there are numerous distinctive characteristics useful in identification. Some of the distinctions are found in the manner in which the flowers are borne on the stem,—whether solitary or multiple from an areole, whether terminal or lateral, whether from unmodified areoles or from specially modified fertile areas. Most cactus flowers are radially symmetrical (Fig. 20), but some are bilaterally symmetrical.

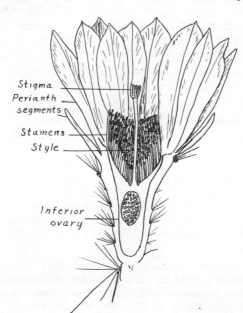

Stigma
Perianth segments
Stamens
Style

Inferior ovary

Figure 20. A radially symmetrical flower of *Echinocereus* in longitudinal section showing inferior ovary, spiny ovary and short floral tube, outer and inner perianth segments, numerous stamens and lobed stigma.

17

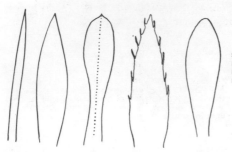

Figure 21. Some shapes of perianth segments (petals or sepals): left to right, linear, lanceolate, spatulate with mucronate tip, lanceolate with ciliate margins, oblanceolate and blunt.

Although many of the most colorful cactus flowers are diurnal, some of the largest ones are nocturnal and are adapted for pollination by moths or by bats. Color may vary from white through green, yellow, red and violet, with yellow the most frequent and bluish colors the rare.

As indicated above, there is little distinction between petals and sepals, and most commonly there is only a transition in color from the outer to the inner perianth segments. The shape may be distinctive, however, whether linear-lanceolate, spatulate, or oblanceolate (Fig. 21), whether marginally smooth or ciliate, terminally blunt, acute or mucronate.

The floral tube (sometimes almost lacking) has a number of distinctive characters,—whether long or short, smooth, scaly, tuberculate, hairy or spiny. The general form, whether cylindrical, tapered or flared, together with the character of the open perianth, gives the shape of the flower: cylindrical, companulate, infundibuliform.

The stamens are always numerous and indefinite in number, but they may be shorter than the perianth (inserted) (see Fig. 20), or longer (exserted) (see Fig. 25).

The stigma may be of distinctive color, lobing or position.

Although cactus fruits are of exceedingly diverse character and of great importance in identification, they are seldom represented in herbarium specimens, and for their lack cactus taxonomy has often suffered difficulties. Most cactus fruits are fleshy and edible by both man and beast, but some are dry, woody and horny. The shape is often distinctive, whether clavate, ovoid, globose, obovoid, truncate or rounded. Some are smooth, spineless, fleshy capsules; others are provided with dry or fleshy scales, others with hairs and bristles, others with wool and spines (Fig. 22).

The characters of mature fruits may usually be determined readily by close examination, and one should be careful not to overlook the importance of fruits in making cactus identifications. A further fruit character often of importance is found in the seed, which sometimes has distinctive color, shape, size, wall sculpturing or specialized mor-phology such as the development of a corky aril (Fig. 23; Fig. 166).

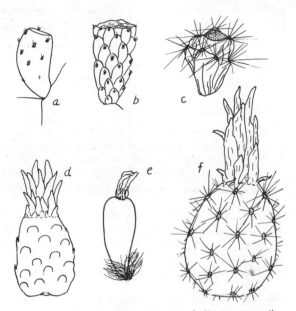

Figure 22. Some kinds of cactus fruits: a, a smooth, fleshy, spineless fruit with glochids (Opuntia); b, a fleshy, tuberculate fruit with glochids (Opuntia); c, a dry, spiny fruit (Opuntia); d, a dry, scaly fruit (Ferocactus); e, smooth, berry-like, naked fruit (Mammillaria); f, spiny, fleshy fruit (Echinocereus).

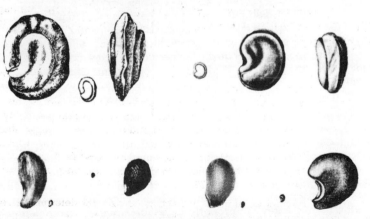

Figure 23. Some kinds of cactus seeds: (the smaller figures in each case are natural size). upper row: Opuntia spp.; Lower row, left to right: Coryphantha; Mammillaria; Ferocactus; Echinomastus.

LITERATURE AND REFERENCES

THE following are the principal references still in print that may be of interest to students using this book. All are available from Abbey Garden Press, 132 W. Union Street, Pasadena, California, which is also publishing headquarters for the Journal of the Cactus and Succulent Society of America ($4.00 per year with membership).

Arizona Cacti—Benson.................183 pp., 29 pp. ill.—$4.25

Cacti and Succulents and How to Grow Them—Haselton.........
.....................................64 pp., 65 ill.—50c

Cacti for the Amateur—Haselton...........142 pp., 160 ill.—$3.65

Colorado Cacti—Boissevain and Davidson.....75 pp., 47 ill.—$3.50

Epiphyllum Handbook—Haselton............250 pp., 170 ill.—$5.00

Cacti of the Southwest—Earle..............108 pp., 122 ill.—$1.50

USE OF THE PICTURED-KEY

THE pictured-key is designed to enable the interested amateur to identify to the species all of the common wild cacti of the United States and our Caribbean islands, as well as a selected few of the most widely and commonly cultivated forms in this country. Little-known species, or those of very limited distribution, are for the most part omitted, but apart from the relatively few rare ones, the student should be able to identify the great majority of the cacti that he may encounter wherever he goes in the United States. Distributional notes are included as an aid to identification, for some species of similar characters have distinctive ranges, and the cultivated, exotic ones may often be recognized quickly by these notes if not by the illustrations.

The student should always be aware that the characters of a well-developed, mature plant are implied in the key, that juvenile plants or immature parts may not serve for identification. Further, he should be aware of the great variation to be found in some of the widespread species and realize that even our most able specialists often find it difficult to recognize specific or varietal characters that show a satisfying degree of constance in these variable plants. Therefore, if your plant does not the first time key out properly to its name, and its characters are not clear-cut, it may be necessary to try alternate legs of the key until a satisfactory result is obtained.

PICTURED-KEY TO THE COMMONER CACTI
OF THE UNITED STATES

1a Plant with persistent, broad, flat leaves; areoles without glochids.
Fig. 24...Pereskia pereskia

1b Leaves small, subulate or cylindric, on young branches only; areoles
with glochids. (See Figs. 19 and 29)...........................2

1c Leaves essentially absent; areoles without glochids............73

Figure 24

Fig. 24. *Pereskia pereskia* (Linnaeus) Karsten
Part of a flowering plant showing broad, persistent leaves and
short spines. Two fruits are shown separately, × 0.56. Puerto Rico and
Florida. Widely grown in the American tropics for its edible fruit
known as West Indian Gooseberry.

21

2a Stamens much longer than petals. Fig. 25...*Nopalea cochenillifera*

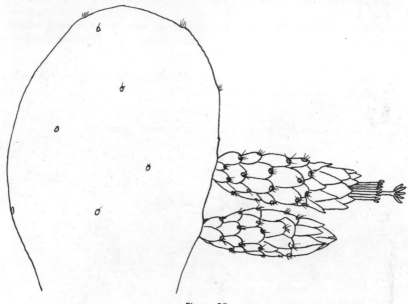

Figure 25

Fig. 25. *Nopalea cochenillifera* (Linnaeus) Salm-Dyck

Outline of a single mature flowering pad showing exserted stamens of the flower, X 0.6. Widely cultivated in the West Indies and tropical America. This plant was named for its importance as a host plant for cochineal insects, source of the crimson dye so important in commerce during the early Spanish colonial days in America. Plants were cultivated in great nopalries (plantations of 50,000 plants or more). The insects were placed on them to multiply and were brushed off into bags two or three times a year.

2b Stamens shorter than petals. (See Fig. 6)..............3 *(Opuntia)*

3a Joints all more or less cylindrical (subgenus *Cylindropuntia*).....4

3b Joints all compressed or flat (subgenus *Platyopuntia*)..........26

4a Spines with papery sheaths. (See Fig. 31).....................5

4b Spines without sheaths.......................................20

5a Spines, at least some of them, solitary in each areole; ultimate branches mostly less than 1 cm. thick..........................6

5b Spines always more than 1 per areole; ultimate branches more
than 1 cm. thick. 9

6a Stem and branches conspicuously marked by flattened, diamond-
shaped tubercles; fruit dry, covered with long. bristle-like spines.
Fig. 26. . . . .*Opuntia ramosissima*

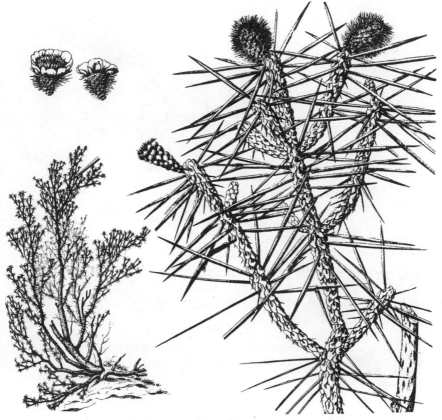

Figure 26

Fig. 26. *Opuntia ramosissima* Engelmann

Habit of a mature plant and detail (× 0.5) of an upper branch showing sheathed spines, diamond-shaped tubercles, flower, and dry, spiny
fruit. A common bushy species in the deserts of southeastern California,
southern Nevada and western Arizona.

6b Tubercles not flattened or diamond-shaped; fruit berry-like, nearly
naked. (See Fig. 22a). 7

7a Ultimate joints 4-7 mm. thick. Fig. 27..........*Opuntia leptocaulis*

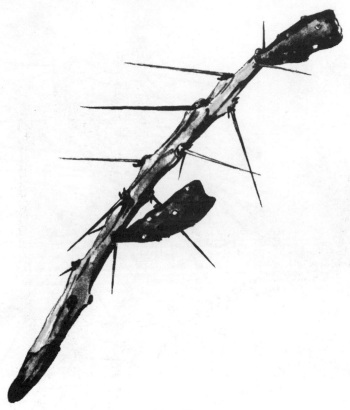

Figure 27

Fig. 27. *Opuntia leptocaulis* De Candolle

A small upper branch bearing fruit, X 1. Bushy, 1-6 ft. high. Widespread in arid lowlands through the southwestern United States.

7b Ultimate joints 8-15 mm. thick..................................8

8a Joints only slightly tuberculate. Fig. 28.........*Opuntia arbuscula*

Figure 28

Fig. 28. *Opuntia arbuscula* Engelmann

Parts of different plants showing young shoot with leaves, an open flower and variations in spines, X 0.8. A tree-like, slender-branched cholla 2-4 feet high. At elevations of 1000-3000 ft., central southern Arizona.

8b Joints manifestly tuberculate. Fig. 29..........*Opuntia kleiniae*

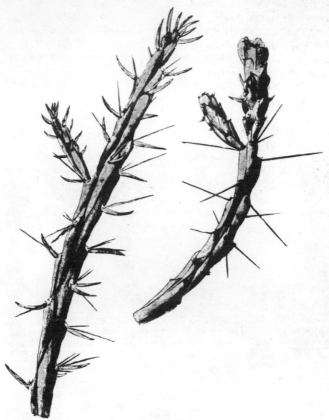

Figure 29

Fig. 29. *Opuntia kleiniae* De Candolle

(Right)—An upper branch with a flower just closed, showing distinct tuberculations. (Left)—A young, growing shoot with leaves. Both ✕ 0.65. This is a shrubby or bushy species 2-3 ft. high at 3000-4000 ft. elevations occurring from southeastern Arizona to Texas.

9a Ultimate branches 2 cm. thick or less..........................10

9b Ultimate branches 2 cm. thick or more........................12

10a Spines white; flowers yellow. Fig. 30.........*Opuntia whipplei*

Fig. 30. *Opuntia whipplei* Engelmann & Bigelow

Upper part of a fruiting plant, ✕ 0.6, and habit of an entire plant, much reduced. This is the common cholla of the juniper-pinyon belt at

26

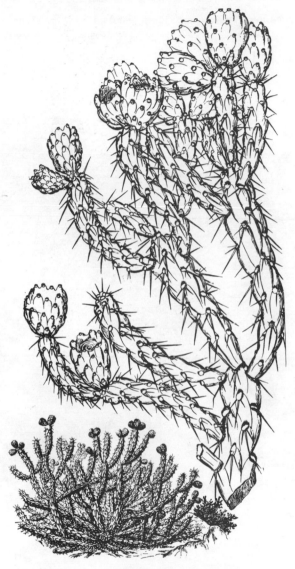

Figure 30

elevations of 4500-7000 feet throughout northern Arizona and New Mexico, southern Utah and western Colorado. It is commonly low and mat-forming, but may be quite erect.

27

10b Spines yellow or brown; flowers greenish....................11

11a Spines yellow. up to 5 cm. long; petals 1.0-1.5 cm: long. Fig. 31..
....*Opuntia davisii*

Figure 31

Fig. 31. *Opuntia davisii* Engelmann & Bigelow
Habit (much reduced) and details of branching, sheathed spines and tuberculate fruit, × 0.6. Somewhat localized in uplands of western Texas and southeastern New Mexico.

11b Spines brown. 2.5 cm. long or less; petals 2.0-2.5 cm. long.......
.... Opuntia viridiflora
This is a somewhat localized species that occurs commonly in
the hills in the vicinity of Santa Fe, New Mexico.

12a Fruit dry. (See Fig. 34c, d)...................................13

12b Fruit fleshy. Fig. 32...15

Fig. 32. Terminal joint of Opuntia fulgida
showing two fleshy, proliferous pendant
fruits, X 1.15.

Figure 32

13a Tubercles elongated, 2-3 times as long as wide..............14

13b Tubercles short, less than twice as long as wide. Fig. 33, 34b,
c, d..*Opuntia echinocarpa*

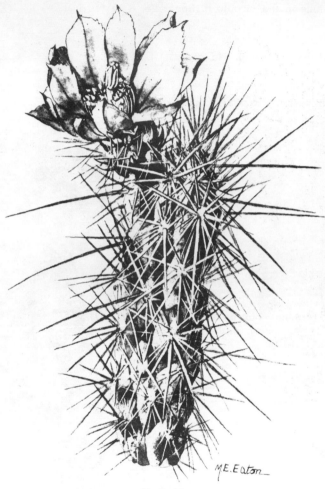

Figure 33

Fig. 33. *Opuntia echinocarpa* Engelmann & Bigelow

A terminal, flowering joint of a well-watered specimen showing
tubercles, × 0.9. Widely distributed on desert mesas and washes at
1000-3000 ft. in western Arizona and southern Nevada, the Mojave
Desert of California and east to southern Utah. A small, erect cholla
2-4 ft. high.

14a Stems conspicuously covered with a mass of spines; fruit long-spiny. Fig. 34a.........................*Opuntia acanthocarpa*

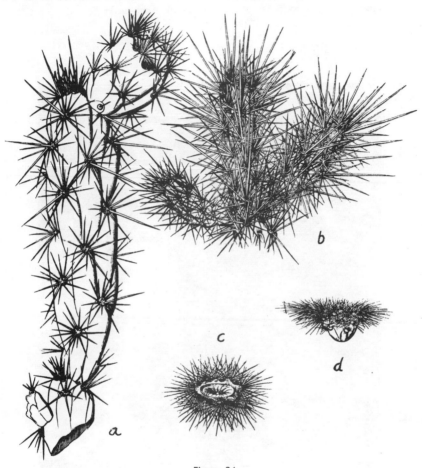

Figure 34

Fig. 34. a, *Opuntia acanthocarpa* Engelmann & Bigelow

An upper branch of a well-watered specimen showing elongated tubercles and a young fruit, X 0.62. This species occurs widely on desert flats and washes of western Arizona and southeastern California, and into southwestern Utah.

b, c, d, *Opuntia echinocarpa* Engelmann & Bigelow

A somewhat dehydrated upper branch and two mature, dry fruits X 0.62. See also Fig. 33.

31

14b Stems not conspicuously covered with spines; fruit short-spiny.
Fig. 35...*Opuntia parryi*
(*Opuntia acanthocarpa* var. *thornberi* will key out here. It is a
bushy species to 5 ft. high in central Arizona.)

Figure 35

Fig. 35. *Opuntia parryi* Engelmann

Upper part of a plant cultivated in the Santa Barbara Botanic Garden. This is a common species of the inland valleys of Southern California west of the deserts.

15a Tubercles of young joints scarcely longer than broad. Fig. 36....
....Opuntia bigelovii

Figure 36

Fig. 36. *Opuntia bigelovii* Engelmann

Habit of a mature plant. This is the Teddy Bear Cactus or Jumping Cholla. The latter name is applied because the barbed spines so readily penetrate shoes, clothing or flesh, and the joints so readily detach themselves that they seem to "jump" at one with often painful result. This is our most easily recognized cholla in the desert lowlands of southeastern California, southern Nevada and western Arizona.

15b Tubercles distinctly longer than broad......................16

16a Tubercles narrow, high, much flattened laterally............17

16b Tubercles broad, low.......................................18

17a Fruit smooth or but slightly tuberculate. Fig. 37..............
....*Opuntia versicolor*

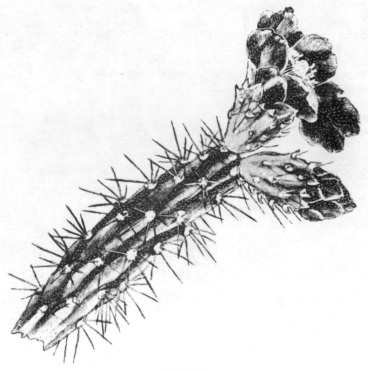

Figure 37

Fig. 37. *Opuntia versicolor* Engelmann

An upper flowering branch showing narrow, elevated tubercles and slightly tuberculate ovaries, × 1. Thus species occurs from 2000-3000 ft. in the deserts of south central Arizona. The flowers are variously colored: yellow, red, green, brown, orange or bronze.

34

17b Fruit manifestly tuberculate. Fig. 38...........*Opuntia imbricata*

Fig. 38. *Opuntia imbricata* (Haworth) De Candolle

A young, growing branch still bearing its leaves and showing the high, narrow tubercles, × 0.75. This is a tall, tree-like cholla up to 9 feet high, common on mesas and foothills of western Texas and New Mexico, to southern Colorado and Oklahoma. Extracts from the fruits were formerly used in Mexico for mordanting cochineal dye. The stems have been used in making canes. It is one of the most formidably spiny of the chollas due to its strongly barbed spines.

Figure 38

35

18a Joints readily detached, freely falling. (See Fig. 32), Fig. 39 . . . . .
. . . . *Opuntia fulgida*

Figure 39

Fig. 39. *Opuntia fulgida* Engelmann

Habit of a mature plant showing the pendant chains of persistent, proliferous fruits. This is the most striking cholla of the southern Arizona deserts. It is erect and tree-like, often forming dense forests of plants 4-6, or up to 15 feet high.

18b Joints not very readily detached, persistent 19

19a Branches slender; fruit not proliferous. Fig. 40................
....*Opuntia spinosior*

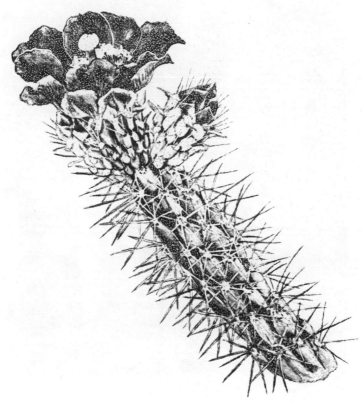

Figure 40

Fig. 40. *Opuntia spinosior* (Engelmann) Toumey

An upper, flowering branch showing the relatively broad, short tubercles, × 1. The flowers are variously colored from white to red, yellow or purple, This is the characteristic smaller, shrubby cholla of the desert grasslands of southeastern Arizona and southwestern New Mexico at elevations from 2000-7000 ft.

19b Branches stout, fruit proliferous. (See Fig. 15), Fig. 41.........
....*Opuntia prolifera*

Figure 41

Fig. 41. *Opuntia prolifera* Engelmann

Habit of a mature plant. This is the characteristic cholla of the coastal hills and offshore islands of southern California. It does not occur in the interior valleys or deserts.

20a Spines distinctly flattened. (See Fig. 42).....................21

20b Spines terete, or only the longest ones somewhat flattened....23

21a Stems stout, the joints 7-15 cm. long........................24

21b Stems more slender and weak, the joints mostly under 7 cm. long 22

22a Bristles on ovary and fruit white. Fig. 42, right....*Opuntia clavata*

22b Bristles on ovary and fruit brown. Fig. 42, left................
...................................*Opuntia stanlyi* var. *parishii*

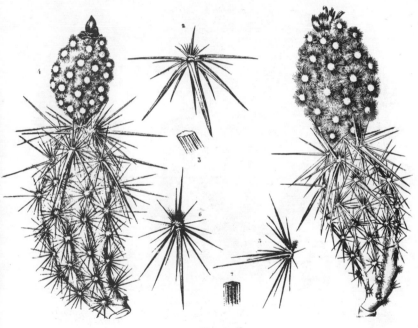

Figure 42

Fig. 42. Left, *Opuntia stanlyi* var. *parishii* (Orcutt) L. Benson; right, *Opuntia clavata* Engelmann

Fruiting joints and spine clusters of each, × 0.62. These are closely related plants. The former occurs in the deserts of eastern California, southern Nevada and northwestern Arizona. The latter occurs in the Navajo country of northeastern Arizona and New Mexico where it is a pest to grazing stock.

23a Flowers pinkish or purple. Fig. 43...........*Opuntia pulchella*

23b Flowers yellow. Fig. 44.....................*Opuntia grahamii*
(*Opuntia schottii* Engelmann is a similar species in western and southern Texas, but has somewhat flattened spines.)
24a Tubercles not joining one another to form ridges on the joint; fruit green or brown..25

24b Tubercles of stem commonly somewhat confluent to form ribs along the joint; fruit yellow...
..............*Opuntia stanlyi* var. *wrightiana* (Baxter) L. Benson
This plant occurs on low desert valley floors of easternmost California and westernmost Arizona.

Figure 43

Fig. 43. *Opuntia pulchella* Engelmann
Part of a flowering plant, × 0.7, a bud and two seeds, enlarged. Alluvial bottoms in southern Nevada and northwestern Arizona.

Fig. 44. *Opuntia grahamii* Engelmann
Habit of an entire small fruiting plant showing thick, fleshy root, clusters of terete spines and seeds, × 0.62. A low, spreading, mound-forming plant of western Texas and southeastern New Mexico.

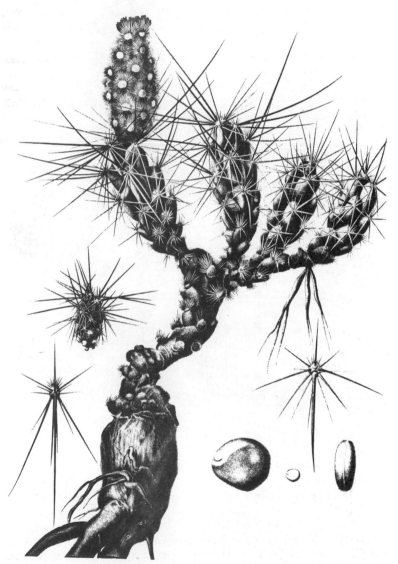

Figure 44

25α Fruit about 2½ inches long, to nearly 1 inch in diameter. Fig. 45. .
.....................................*Opuntia stanlyi* var. *stanlyi*

Figure 45

~Fig. 45. *Opuntia stanlyi* Engelmann var. *stanlyi*
   Two joints of a mature, fruiting plant, × 0.62. Southeastern Arizona
and southwestern New Mexico.

25b Fruit about 1½-2 inches long, ½ inch in diameter ....
.................*Opuntia stanlyi* var. *kunzei* (Rose) L. Benson
This plant occurs on plains at 1000-2000 ft. in the middle of south-
ernmost Arizona, in the vicinity of Organ Pipe Cactus National
Monument.

26a Plants branching from near the base, or if erect, the trunk distinctly jointed; flowers mostly large.........................28

26b Plants with erect, cylindrical unjointed trunks, the branches with
flat joints 27

27a Flowers small; lateral joints linear-obovate, often curved. Fig.
46a.......................................*Opuntia moniliformis*

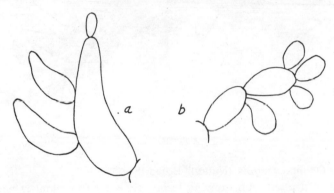

Figure 46

Fig. 46. Diagrams of lateral-branch shapes of (a) *Opuntia moniliformis*
(Linnaeus) Haworth, and (b) *Opuntia ammophila* Small.
    The former is a large, tree-like form 8-12 feet tall with heavy trunk,
growing in Puerto Rico. The latter is a smaller, erect plant (3-6 ft.)
found on inland sand dunes of peninsular Florida and said to be the
most conspicuous native prickly pear of Florida.

27b Flowers large; lateral joints obovate to elliptic. Fig. 46b.........
....*Opuntia ammophila*

28a Fruit a juicy berry...36

28b Fruit dry, not juicy.......................................29

29a Joints readily detached, turgid, some of them subterete or sub-globose. Fig. 47................................*Opuntia fragilis*

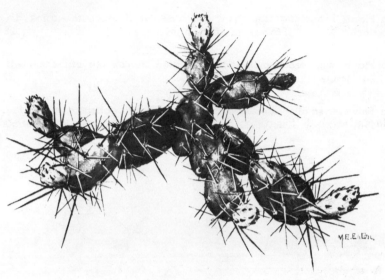

Figure 47

Fig. 47. *Opuntia fragilis* (Nuttall) Haworth

Habit of a plant with growing branches, × 1. This plant is widely distributed over the Great Plains from Wisconsin to central Kansas and northwestern Texas, westward through northern Arizona, Utah, Montana, and to the drier parts of Oregon and Washington. It is a troublesome grassland pest to grazing animals.

29b Joints not readily detached, usually flat and thin.............30

30a Spines, or some of them, very long, flexible and bristle-like....35

30b Spines stiff, acicular or subulate.............................31

Fig. 48. *Opuntia juniperina* Britton & Rose

A single joint, × 0.5. This species is rather local in the juniper belt about San Juan County, New Mexico.

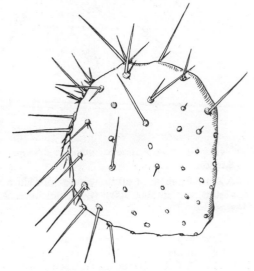

Figure 48

33a Flowers yellow or red; nearly all areoles bearing spines, the longest ones 4.5-7.5 or 10 cm long. Fig. 49.........................
....................................*Opuntia erinacea* var. *hystricina*

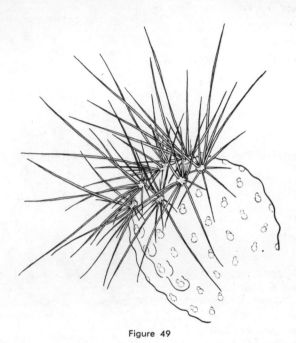

Figure 49

Fig. 49. *Opuntia erinacea* var. *hystricina* (Engelmann & Bigelow) L. Benson

A single joint (not all the spines are shown), × 0.5. This plant occurs at elevations of 5000-7000 ft. in northern Arizona and northern New Mexico.

33b Flowers red (sometimes yellow); only distal areoles spine bearing, the longest ones 2.5-3.7 cm. long.............................
.....*Opuntia erinacea* var. *xanthostema* (K. Schuman) L. Benson
This is probably the most abundant cactus in the pinyon and yellow pine forests of northern Arizona and New Mexico and west to the Mt. Whitney region of California.

34a Ovary and fruit naked, without spines........................
....................*Opuntia sphaerocarpa* Engelman & Bigelow
This is a rather local species in the mountains in the vicinity of Albuquerque, New Mexico.

34b Ovary and fruit with spines. (See Fig. 13.)...*Opuntia polyacantha*

35a Flowers 4-5 cm. long. Fig. 50.....................................
.........................*Opuntia polyacantha* var. *trichophora*

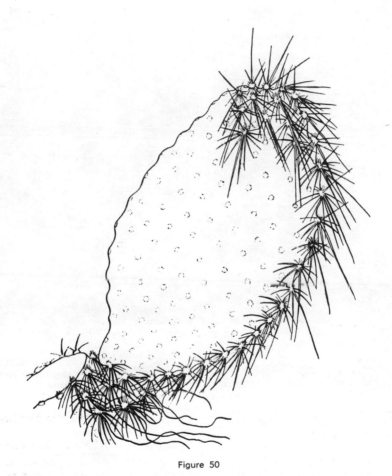

Figure 50

Fig. 50. *Opuntia polyacantha* var. *trichophora* (Engelmann & Bigelow) Coulter

A single joint (only part of spines drawn) showing characteristic thread-like spines at base of branches, × 0.75. Occurs on sandy plains and hills from northeastern Arizona to Oklahoma.

35b Flowers 5-6 cm. long.............*Opuntia erinacea* var. *erinacea*
The very long-spined *O. erinacea* var. *ursina* (Weber) Parish (Fig. 51) is the most striking form of this species.

Figure 51

Fig. 51. *Opuntia erinacea* var. *ursina* (Weber) Parish
Habit of a clump of mature plants. This plant is occasional in the Mojave Desert region of California and Arizona and is fast disappearing because of its attractiveness and demand for cultivation. It is known as the Grizzly Bear Cactus.

36a Joints readily detached.....................................37

36b Joints not readily detached, persistent.......................41

37a Low-growing, mostly small-jointed species...................38

37b Taller, larger-jointed (7-20 cm. long). Fig. 52...*Opuntia antillana*

Fig. 52. *Opuntia antillana* Britton & Rose
A small portion of a plant,
× 0.33. Widely distributed in
the West Indies. Forming thickets in Puerto Rico and the Virgin Islands. Often the most
abundant cactus in these areas.

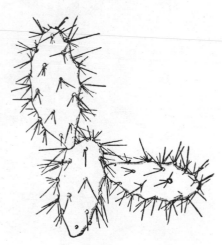

Figure 52

38a Spines slender, acicular.....................................39

38b Spines subulate 40

49

39a Joints narrow, 5-16 cm. long; spines usually numerous; flowers yellow. Fig. 53...............................*Opuntia repens*

Figure 53

Fig. 53. *Opuntia repens* Bello

A small plant and an open flower, × 0.62. Common in Puerto Rico and the Virgin Islands where it is often a troublesome weed. It spreads readily because of its fragile, clinging joints.

39b Joints oblong, 4-8 cm.; spines mostly 3 to an areole; flowers brown-
ish-yellow. Fig. 54............................*Opuntia triacantha*

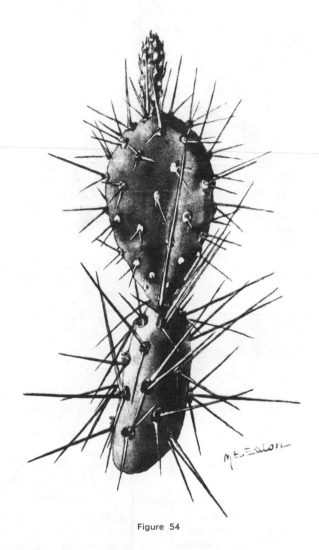

Figure 54

Fig. 54. *Opuntia triacantha* (Willdenow) Sweet

A small part of a growing plant, × 1.05. Common on flats and
low hills near the sea in the Virgin Islands and Puerto Rico.

40a Joints with only slightly undulate margins. Fig. 55..............
....Opuntia drummondii

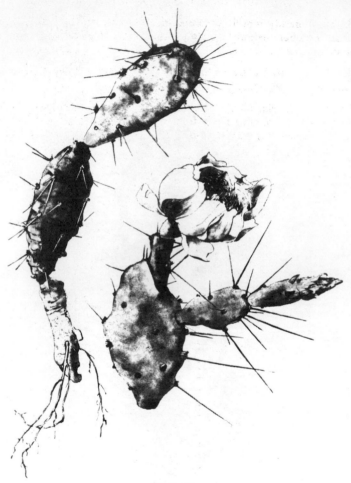

Figure 55

Fig. 55. *Opuntia drummondii* Graham

A small rooted plant and a flowering joint, × 0.66. Grows in sandy soil, often along the coast and islands from northern Florida to North Carolina. *Opuntia tracyi* Britton is a similar species with prominently elevated areoles giving the margins of the joints a strongly undulate outline. It grows from southern Mississippi to southeastern Georgia and northern Florida.

40b Joints with very prominently undulate margins and abundant glochids...*Opuntia tracyi*
(See note under Fig. 55)

41a Areoles usually small, 1-2 mm. in diameter, not elevated, mostly close together, usually densely filled with glochids and with few or no spines..42

41b Areoles larger, mostly distant, spiny or spineless, but the glochids usually not especially conspicuous.........................43

42a Flowers red. Fig. 56..........................*Opuntia basilaris*
This species branches more from the base and tends to have thinner joints than *Opuntia treleasei* (Fig. 57) which is closely related.

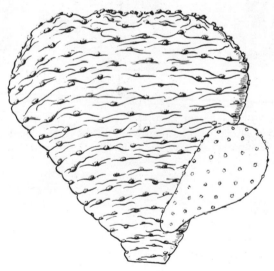

Figure 56

Fig. 56. *Opuntia basilaris* Engelmann & Bigelow
Old and young joints, X 0.5. This is a variable species at low elevations in the deserts of western Arizona, eastern California, southern Nevada and Utah. It is commonly known as Beaver Tail and, appearing harmless, is often handled with distressing results because of the miriad microscopic glochids.

Figure 57

Fig. 57. *Opuntia treleasei* Coulter

Habit of a clumping plant growing in its rather local home in the Tehachapi Mountains region of southern California.

42b Flowers yellow..................................*Opuntia rufida*
This is a more erect species than the last. It grows in the Big Bend district of Texas where it is known as Blind Pear.

43a Plants prostrate and spreading..............................44

43b Plants bushy (sometimes spreading, the lower joints lying on edge, as in *Opuntia stricta* and *O. ballii*), semi-erect or erect...54

44a Flowers purple. Fig. 58 . . . . *Opuntia pottsii*

Fig. 58. *Opuntia pottsii*
Salm-Dyck

A single joint, X 0.4.
This species occurs along
the southern boundary of
New Mexico and along
the Rio Grande of Texas.
The large purple flowers
and fleshy roots are dis-
tinctive.

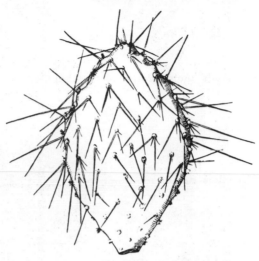

Figure 58

44b Flowers yellow **45**
45a Spines none, or only 1 or 2 at an areole **46**
45b Spines, when present, mostly 2 or more at an areole **51**
46a Joints 16-24 cm. long. Fig. 59 . . . . *Opuntia tardospina* (in part)

Fig. 59. *Opuntia tardo-
spina* Griffiths

A single joint with rela-
tively short spines, of a
plant collected north of
Dallas, Texas. Occurs in
eastern Texas. X about
0.35.

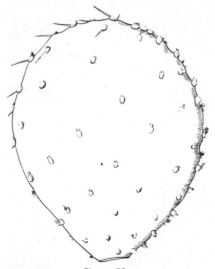

Figure 59

55

46b Joints less than 16 cm. long.................................. 47

47a Joints bluish-green; roots tuber-like......................... 48

47b Joints green; roots not tuberous............................. 49

48a Fruits clavate; joints thin, usually spineless. Fig. 60............
.... *Opuntia allairei*

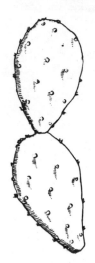

Fig. 60. *Opuntia allairei* Griffiths

Two spineless joints, × 0.66. Spines may be present, 1-3 and less than 2.5 cm. long. The plant occurs in southern Texas and western Louisiana.

Figure 60

48b Fruits obovoid; joints turgid. Fig. 61...........*Opuntia pollardii*

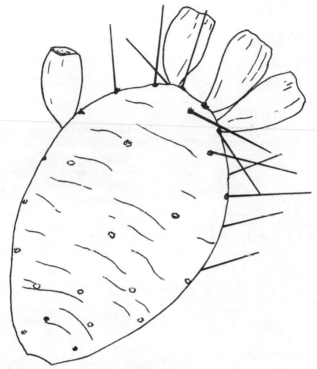

Figure 61

Fig. 61. *Opuntia pollardii* Britton & Rose

A single fruiting joint, ✕ 0.55, of a plant from Alabama. This is a species of the Atlantic coastal plain from North Carolina to northern Florida, and on the Gulf coast of Alabama and Mississippi.

49a Flowers 8 cm. broad or less.................................50

49b Flowers 10-12 cm. broad. Fig. 62..........*Opuntia grandiflora*

50a Joints orbicular or a little longer than wide. Fig. 63............
....*Opuntia compressa*

Fig. 62. *Opuntia grandiflora* Engelmann

A flowering joint and a fruit, × 0.4. Occurs in eastern Texas. This may ultimately prove simply to be a variety of *Opuntia compressa*.

Figure 62

Fig. 63. *Opuntia compressa* (Salisbury) MacBride var. *compressa*

A flowering joint, × 1.1. This is the most widespread of our eastern prickly pears, and the first to have been described from this country. It occurs in rocky and sandy places from Massachusetts to Virginia and in the mountains of Georgia and central Alabama westward to northern Illinois, eastern Missouri and Tennessee. This is the *Opuntia opuntia* of some authors.

Figure 63

50b Joints oblong, much longer than wide. Fig. 64.................
....*Opuntia macrarthra*

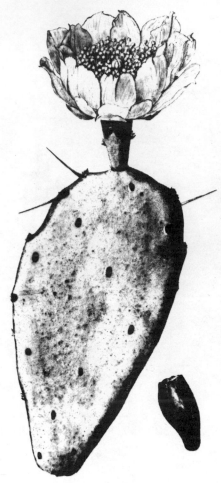

Fig. 64. *Opuntia macrarthra* Gibbes

A flowering joint and a fruit, × 0.6. This plant occurs along the coast of South Carolina.

Figure 64

51a Roots tuberous 52

51b Roots not tuberous...53

52a Joints with few or no spines at most areoles. Fig. 65...........
.............................*Opuntia compressa* var. *macrorhiza*

Figure 65

Fig. 65. *Opuntia compressa* var. *macrorhiza* (Engelmann) L. Benson
    A flowering plant showing tuberous roots; also a fruit. This variety occurs from Missouri and Kansas to Texas and westward to Arizona at elevations of 4500-6000 ft. The western forms become more spiny.

52b Joints with 1-4 spines in upper areoles...*Opuntia mackensenii* Rose
    This plant is known from the vicinity of Kerr County, Texas, and may be a variant of *Opuntia compressa*.

53a Spines several, often 6-8, white to light brown, slender (see step 64a and Fig. 73)...................*Opuntia phaeacantha* (in part)

53b Spines in twos or threes, dark brown, stout....................
....................................*Opuntia fuscoatra* Engelmann
    This plant is known from "sterile" places of prairies west of Houston, Texas, but is probably not a distinct species.

61

54a Fruit small, 2 cm. long or less. Fig. 66.............*Opuntia ballii*

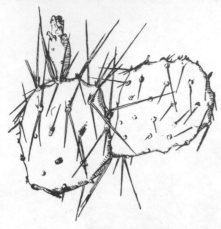

Fig. 66. *Opuntia ballii* Rose

Two joints showing a fruit, × 0.5. This small-fruited plant grows in western Texas, especially on the dry mesa beyond Pecos.

Figure 66

54b Fruit larger, 2.5-6 cm. long....................................55

55a Roots fusiform or tuberous. Fig. 67.............*Opuntia austrina*

Figure 67

Fig. 67. *Opuntia austrina* Small

An upper part of a flowering plant, × 0.4. This plant of distinctive root character occurs in southern Florida.

55b Roots not fusiform or tuberous...............................56

56a Spines distinctly banded. Fig. 68......*Opuntia dillenii* (in part)

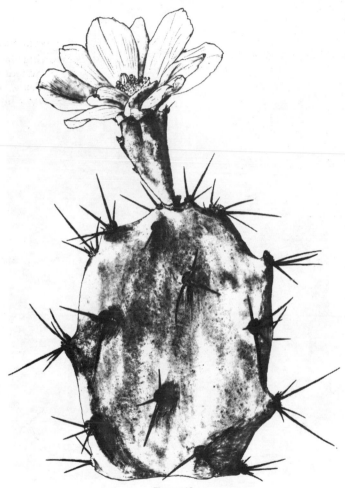

Figure 68

Fig. 68. *Opuntia dillenii* (Ker-Gawler) Haworth

An upper flowering joint, × 0.5. This species from the coasts of South Carolina and Florida extends through the West Indies to South America. It became introduced widely throughout the world during early Spanish times and became a "pest pear" in south India and Australia. The plant is extremely variable in size, joint-shape and spination.

56b Spines not banded..57

57a Joints very large, 30-50 cm. long, essentially spineless. Fig. 69...
....*Opuntia ficus-indica*

Figure 69

Fig. 69. *Opuntia ficus-indica* (Linnaeus) Miller

Habit of a cultivated plant in Santa Ynez, California. This species is widely cultivated for fruit and forage in warmer parts of the world, and its origin probably dates to prehistoric times, for its native home is unknown. It has run wild in many places along the Mediterranean, the Red Sea and in Africa.

57b Joints usually less than 30 cm. long (except *Opuntia linguiformis*), spiny, or at least with some conspicuous spines.............58

58a Spines brown, at least at base or tip, but not yellow........59

58b Spines yellow, except sometimes for a brown base..........66

59a Joints thin; spines, when present, very long and confined to the upper and middle areoles.................................60

59b Joints thick; spines not confined to upper and middle areoles..62

60a Plants dull, dark green; spines 4-5 cm. long or less. (See Fig. 59)..
....*Opuntia tardospina* (in part)

60b Plants often bluish to purplish.............................61

61a Spines lacking from most areoles; some areoles with a single, setaceous, deflexed spine; joints reddish-purple. Fig. 70........
..........................*Opuntia gosseliniana* var. *santa-rita*

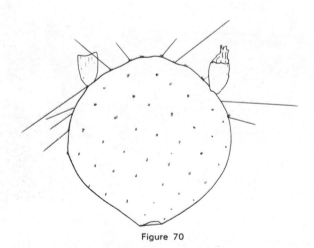

Figure 70

Fig. 70. *Opuntia gosseliniana* var. *santa-rita* (Griffiths & Hare) L. Benson
    A joint with old flower and young fruit, X 0.25. Occasional in foothill grassland areas of Arizona at 3000 to 4000 ft. Easily recognized by the purplish color of the joints.

61b Spines usually present in upper areoles, 1-3, up to 12 cm. long;
joints blue-green tinged with purple in growth, mahogany red in
drought. Fig. 71..........................*Opuntia macrocentra*

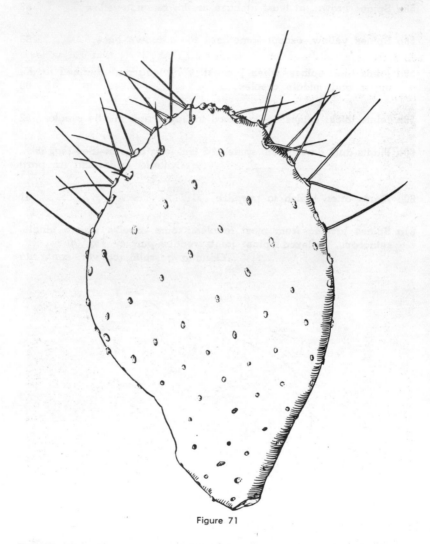

Figure 71

Fig. 71. *Opuntia macrocentra* Engelmann

A somewhat oblong joint, × 0.5. This bushy species 2-3 feet high
from western Texas to eastern Arizona, is a more spiny plant than
O. *gosseliniana*.

62a Joints seldom over 15 cm. broad; plants usually relatively low; spines terete or slightly flattened 63

62b Joints mostly over 15 cm. broad; plants relatively tall; spines commonly in part flattened 65

63a Flowers yellow 64

63b Flowers reddish-salmon to magenta. Fig. 72 ..... *Opuntia vaseyi* (Considered by some authors a variety of O. *occidentalis*.)

Figure 72

Fig. 72. *Opuntia vaseyi* (Coulter) Britton & Rose

Habit of a plant in nature. This is a common thicket plant on the ocean side of the coast range in southern California where its reddish-salmon flowers make it easily recognized. This photo shows a small spreading plant to illustrate the low habit often seen in this species and in O. *covillei*.

64a Spines subulate, brown, at least in part. Fig. 73. (See step 53a)
.................................*Opuntia phaeacantha* (in part)
64b Spines acicular, nearly white when young....................
.................................*Opuntia covillei* Britton & Rose
This is the common yellow-flowered bushy prickly pear of the
interior valleys of southern California where it grows with the
red-flowered O. *vaseyi*. Both of these are considered by some
authors to be varieties of O. *occidentalis*.

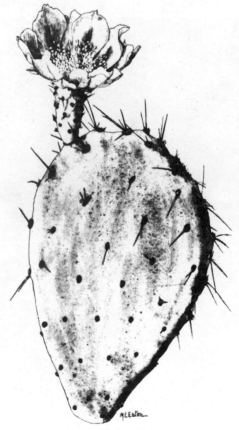

Figure 73

Fig. 73. *Opuntia phaeacantha* Engelmann

A flowering joint, × 0.4. This is the most widely distributed and
abundant prickly pear in Arizona, and extends into southern Nevada,
Utah and New Mexico. It hybridizes with O. *engelmannii*, and many
puzzling variants are to be found.

65a Spines clear brownish throughout, often somewhat curved. (See Fig. 80)..............*Opuntia occidentalis* Engelmann & Bigelow
This is a variable species of southern California considered by some authors to include several named varieties otherwise considered species. It is, for instance, closely related to, and may include *Opuntia littoralis* of similar range in southern California, although apparently occurring more extensively inland.

65b Spines with dark brownish or reddish bases, straight. Fig. 74....
....*Opuntia engelmannii*

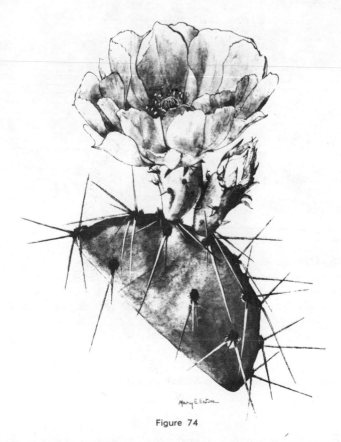

Figure 74

Fig. 74. *Opuntia engelmannii* Salm-Dyck
Upper part of a flowering joint, × 0.5. This is a widely distributed and variable plant to which many scientific names have been applied. It occurs throughout most of southern Arizona and eastward through New Mexico to Texas.

66a Spines nearly setaceous, most of them deflexed. Fig. 75 . . . .
. . . .*Opuntia chlorotica*

Figure 75

Fig. 75. *Opuntia chlorotica* Engelmann & Bigelow

This arborescent prickly pear forms a small, erect tree 3-6 feet high. Its abundant, deflexed, slender yellow spines are distinctive. It is characteristic of low mountains, at about 3000 feet or more, in Arizona and extending to New Mexico and Utah.

66b Spines, when present, acicular to subulate 67

67a Joints often spineless or with 1-2 spines at some of the areoles . . . 68

67b Joints usually manifestly spiny; spines 2 or more at an areole . . . 69

68a Plants tall; spines sparse, mostly 1 cm. long or less. Fig. 76.....
....Opuntia laevis

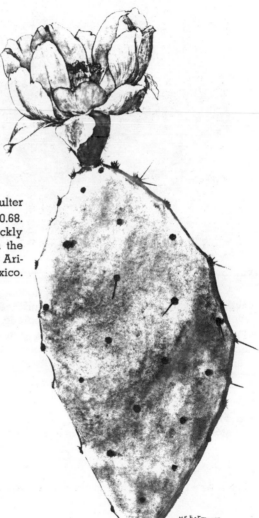

Fig. 76. *Opuntia laevis* Coulter
A flowering joint, × 0.68.
Known as the Spineless Prickly
Pear, this plant is found in the
mountains of southeastern Ari-
zona and adjacent New Mexico.

Figure 76

68b Plants depressed, bushy or spreading; spines commonly very sparse, 1-4 cm. long. Fig. 77.................*Opuntia stricta*

Figure 77

Fig. 77. *Opuntia stricta* Haworth

A flowering joint, × 0.9. Native to Florida and the Gulf coast to southern Texas this species was introduced into Australia where in Queensland and New South Wales it spread rapidly over thousands of acres of grazing land and became the principal plant pest.

69a Margins of joints commonly strongly undulate; spines mostly stout, commonly flattened and mottled. (See Fig. 68)...........
....................................*Opuntia dillenii* (in part)

69b Margins of joints not so strongly undulate; spines acicular to subulate, terete or slightly flattened at the base, not mottled...70

70a Joints elongate-lanceolate or oblong, several times longer than
    wide. Fig. 78..............................*Opuntia linguiformis*

Fig. 78. *Opuntia linguiformis* Griffiths (Cow's Tongue Cactus)

A single flowering joint, × 0.42.
This is the most distinctively
formed of the prickly pears and
has come widely into cultivation
from small wild colonies in the
vicinity of San Antonio, Texas.

Figure 78

73

71b Areoles mostly 2.5-4.0 cm. apart. Fig. 79....*Opuntia lindheimeri*

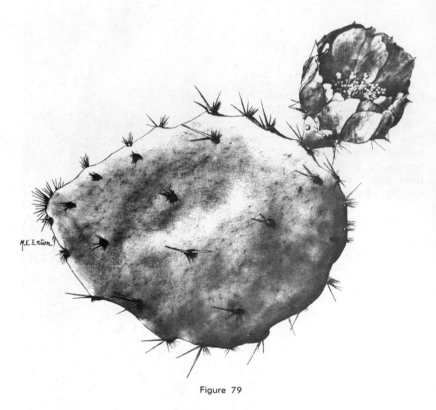

Figure 79

Fig. 79. *Opuntia lindheimeri* Engelmann

A flowering joint, × 0.55. This is a widely variable erect, large prickly pear of southwestern Louisiana and southeastern Texas. Its flowers range from yellow to red.

72a Areoles spiny; spines nearly clear yellow, 1-2 cm. long. Fig. 80..
....Opuntia littoralis
(Considered by some authors a variety of O. occidentalis.)

Figure 80

Fig. 80. *Opuntia littoralis* (Engelmann) Cockerell

Habit of a plant in nature. This is a coastal species inhabiting near-ocean hills of southern California and its adjacent islands. Its range apparently overlaps that of O. *occidentalis*, and distinctions between these two are difficult.

72b Areoles often spineless, with long glochids; spines, where present, brown at the base, long and slender, 3.0-5.5 cm. long. Fig. 81....
....*Opuntia aciculata*

Figure 81

Fig. 81. *Opuntia aciculata* Griffiths

This is a quite localized species in southern Texas in the vicinity of Laredo. The figure is of a flowering joint (× 0.65) showing the long glochids but none of the occasional long slender spines.

73a Flowers minute, less than 3 mm. long; joints cylindrical, 3-5 mm. in diam. Fig. 82..............................*Rhipsalis cassutha*

73b Flowers larger, more than 1 cm. long; joints cylindrical, flat or ribbed, 6 mm. to 65 cm. in diam..............................**74**

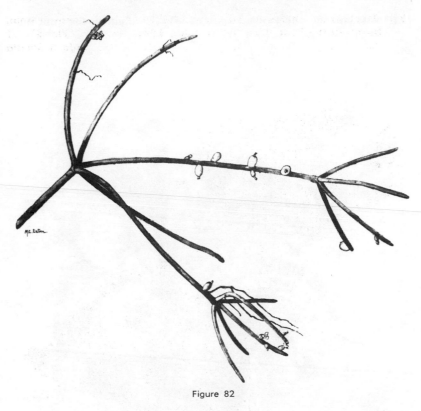

Figure 82

Fig. 82. *Rhipsalis cassutha* Gaertner

Part of a flowering and fruiting plant, × 0.66. This plant hangs as an epiphyte from the branches and trunks of large trees in tropical areas of Florida and the West Indies. It is the commonest of several members of this genus cultivated as hanging basket plants.

74a Areoles mostly spineless; joints flat.........................75

74b Areoles mostly spine-bearing; joints cylindrical, ribbed, angled or tubercled, but not flat...................................76

75a Joints oblong, with toothed margins. Fig. 83..*Zygocactus truncatus*

Figure 83

Fig. 83. *Zygocactus truncatus* (Haworth) Schumann

This is the widely cultivated Christmas Cactus of this country and England where it has been grown since 1818. There are a number of garden varieties with various flower characters. The plant originally came from Brazil.

75b Joints very long, strap-shaped, without toothed margins. Fig. 84..
............................*Epiphyllum* species and hybrids

76a Flowers and spines borne at the same areoles................77

76b Flowers and spines borne at different areoles..............138

Figure 84

Fig. 84. *Epiphyllum ackermannii* Haworth

This is one of a great variety of hybrid "orchid cacti" widely grown now in glass houses and shade houses for their brilliantly colored flowers. Most of the wild species occur in Central America.

80a Margin of stems horny. Fig. 85............*Hylocereus undatus*

80b Margins of stems not horny. Fig. 86.........*Hylocereus trigonus*

Figure 85

Fig. 85. *Hylocereus undatus* (Haworth) Britton & Rose

Part of a flowering stem, × 0.36. This plant is widely cultivated in tropical areas. It forms the famous Punahou School hedge in Honolulu which produces over 5000 flowers in a night.

Fig. 86. *Hylocereus trigonus* (Haworth) Safford

Part of a fruiting stem, × 0.57. This is a wild species of Puerto Rico and the Virgin Islands, extensively clambering over bushes and rocks, reaching 30 feet in length.

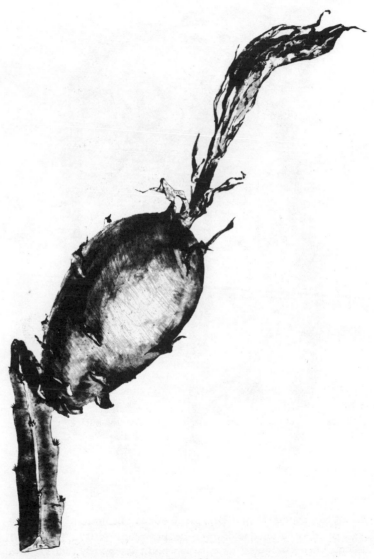

Figure 86

81a Flowers very large, 12-18 cm. long, white, nocturnal.........82

81b Flowers 7-8 cm. long, pink, diurnal. Fig. 87....................
...................................*Aporocactus flagelliformis*

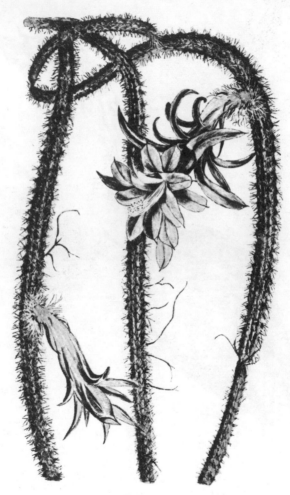

Figure 87

Fig. 87. *Aporocactus flagelliformis* (Linnaeus) Lemaire

Three pendant branches from a basket plant, × 0.7. The Rat Tail Cactus has been cultivated as a house plant for nearly 300 years and is unknown in the wild state.

82a Areoles of the ovary and flower tube bearing long hairs; flowers about 18 cm. long. Fig. 88............*Selenicereus grandiflorus*

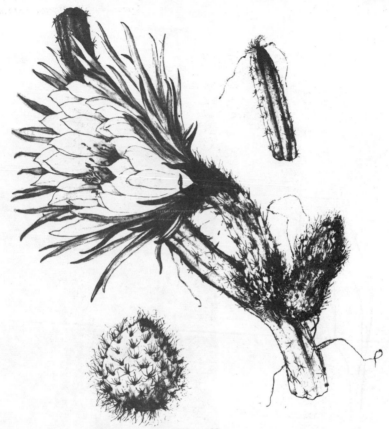

Figure 88

Fig. 88. *Selenicereus grandiflorus* (Linnaeus) Britton & Rose

Flower, bud, fruit and stem, × 0.5. This is another of the several kinds of Night Blooming Cereus that are widely cultivated for their grand flowers. The figure shows an open flower, a hairy bud and a maturing fruit. Several aerial roots appear on the section of stem.

82b Areoles of flower tube and ovary without long hairs...........
............*Selenicereus spinulosus* (De Candolle) Britton & Rose
This is our only native member of the group, reaching up from Mexico into southeastern Texas.

83a Flowers 2 to several at an areole, 3-4 cm. long. Figs. 89, 90 and
97 . . . .*Lophocereus schottii*

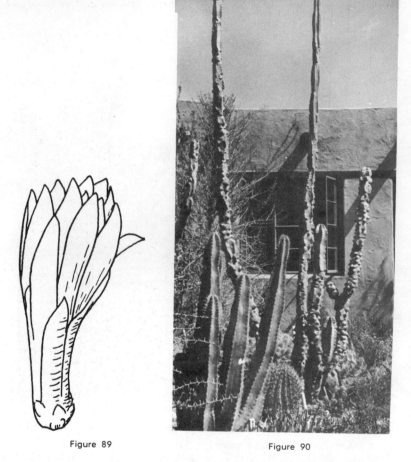

Figure 89   Figure 90

Figs. 89 and 90. *Lophocereus schottii* (Engelmann) Britton & Rose
    Fig. 89. A flower, × 1.6. Fig. 90. A cultivated plant of the normal form in the foreground and a large example of the rare monstrose form behind. This is a Mexican candelabra cactus that occurs in our Organ Pipe Cactus National Monument in Arizona. (See Fig. 97.) Its long bristly spines in the flowering areoles are distinctive.

83b Flowers solitary at the areoles, mostly more than 5 cm. long. . . . 84

84a Ovary naked or with but a few scales. (See Fig. 93).........85

84b Ovary bearing scales with hairs, spines or bristles in their axils..88

85a Perianth funnelform, elongated. Fig. 91..........Cereus species

Figure 91

Fig. 91. Cereus species

Several species and a great many hybrid forms of this genus are grown in cactus gardens and as decorative plants in warm parts of the country. Most of them assume large candelabrum-like form (left figure) and all have large, white flowers opening at night (right figure).

85b Perianth short-campanulate; plant with many low ribs.........86

86a Flowering areoles without wool, or the wool very short.......87

86b Flowering areoles definitely long-wooly. Fig. 92...............
....*Cephalocereus royenii*

Figure 92

Fig. 92. *Cephalocereus royenii* (Linnaeus) Britton & Rose

Part of a flowering plant showing tufts of wool from flowering areoles. This plant occurs in drier parts of Puerto Rico and the Virgin Islands.

87a Plant greyish-green; all perianth segments rounded. Fig. 93.....
....*Cephalocereus deeringii*

87b Plant glaucous green when young; outer perianth segments acute.
.........................*Cephalocereus keyensis* Britton & Rose
Originally native to the southern Florida keys.

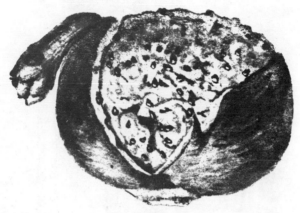

Figure 93

Fig. 93. Cephalocereus deeringii Small
    A mature fruit showing the smooth, spineless ovary wall, the per-sistent, dry perianth and the fleshy pulp, × 1.25. This tall, slender species was formerly abundant on some of the Florida keys, but has been severely restricted in nature by land developments. The same is true of *Cephalocereus keyensis* Britton & Rose, which is nearly extinct in nature and now is to be found mainly in gardens of southern Florida.

88a Stems with 4-5 ribs...89

88b Stems with 8 to many ribs..................................90

89a Roots fibrous; stems arching, the spines 1-4 cm. long...........
...............*Leptocereus quadricostatus (Bello) Britton & Rose*
This plant forms thickets on the dry southwestern part of Puerto Rico. Like other species of *Leptocereus*, (see Fig. 10) this is a rare, local plant approaching extinction by the continued restriction of its small habitat.

89b Roots enormous, fleshy; stems erect, slender, the spines very small. Fig. 94..*Peniocereus greggii*

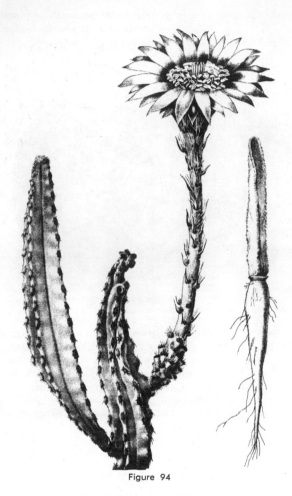

Figure 94

Fig. 94. *Peniocereus greggii* (Engelmann) Britton & Rose

Upper part of a flowering plant, and a very young plant showing early stage in the development of the huge fleshy root, × 0.6. This is the Queen of the Night, a night flowering cereus of southern Arizona, New Mexico and western Texas. It grows among sage brush and is difficult to find except when in flower because of the dead-stick-like branches.

90a Stems 6-10 mm. thick; roots tuberous. Fig. 95...*Wilcoxia poselgeri*

Fig. 95. *Wilcoxia po-selgeri (Lemaire)* Britton & Rose

A cluster of tuberous roots, X 0.75. This is a strange little obscure plant of southern Texas that hides itself in clumps of brush. Its large, showy fragrant flowers give it away from March to May. It is called Lead Pencil Cactus and does best in cultivation when grafted on a strong stock.

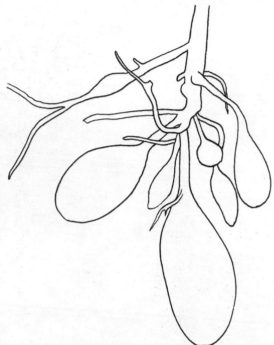

Figure 95

90b Stems more than 3 cm. in diameter; roots not especially fleshy..91

91a Flowers short-campanulate, with short tubes. (See Fig. 98).....92

91b. Flowers long-funnelform or salverform, the tube more or less long. (See Fig. 100).................................94

92a Plants gigantic, columnar at first, 30-65 cm. in diameter, later with branches (see Fig. 11). Fig. 96...............Carnegiea gigantea

Figure 96

Fig. 96. *Carnegiea gigantea* (Engelmann) Britton & Rose

Two mature, branched, flowering plants in the Desert Botanical Garden near Phoenix, Arizona. In the lower left is seen the rare, fan-shaped "crested" form of the Giant Cactus. This species occurs throughout most of southern Arizona and is the most spectacular desert plant of our country. The Indian name is Saguaro, and Saguaro National Monument, near Tucson, Arizona, preserves an especially rich forest of this giant succulent.

92b Plants candelabra-form, the branches 7-20 cm. in diameter.....93

93a Ribs 12-17. Fig. 97.....................*Lemaireocereus thurberi*

Figure 97

Fig. 97. *Lemaireocereus thurberi* (Engelmann) Britton & Rose

A mature plant (on the right) growing in Organ Pipe Cactus National Monument with *Lophocereus schottii*. This species is the *pitahya dulce* of Mexico and is widely distributed in that country, but reaches our borders only in southern Arizona where magnificent stands of these and other giant cacti so inspired naturalists that national monuments were established to preserve them.

93b Ribs mostly 9-10. Fig. 98.................Lemaireocerus hystrix

Figure 98

Fig. 98. *Lemaireocereus hystrix* (Haworth) Britton & Rose

A flower and a fruit, X 0.7. This is a large, candelabrum cactus of the West Indies, found in our territory on the dry islands of Puerto Rico.

94a Scales of ovary with woolly axils. Fig. 99..*Trichocereus spachianus*

Fig. 99. *Trichocereus spachianus* (Lemaire) Riccobono

This species has splendid flowers and is hardy enough to withstand considerable frost. It is one of the most widely cultivated of South American night blooming cerei. Its native home is in Argentina. This plant was flowering in Santa Ynez, California, in July, 1961.

Figure 99

94b Scales of ovary with spines and bristles.....................95

95a Stems ribbed. Fig. 100.................*Nyctocereus serpentinus*

Figure 100

Fig. 100. *Nyctocereus serpentinus* (Lagasca & Rodrigues) Britton & Rose

A short section of a stem bearing an open flower, × 0.5. This is one of our most widely cultivated night blooming cerei. The stems grow in an erect cluster, branched from the base, but in age become clambering.

94

95b Stems angled. Fig. 101...............*Acanthocereus pentagonus*

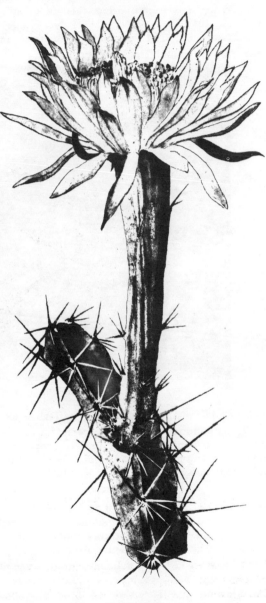

Fig. 101. *Acanthocere-
us pentagonus* (Lin-
naeus) Britton &
Rose

Part of a flowering
branch, × 0.8. This
clambering, spiny plant
with 3-angled stems
grows wild along the
coast of Texas and in
the Florida keys.

Figure 101

95

Figure 102

Fig. 102. *Echinopsis multiplex* (Pfeiffer) Zuccarini

This abundantly flowering species of southern Brazil is very widely grown as a pot plant and is readily propagated from small heads that develop around the base of older plants. The hairyness of the flower tube and ovary may be seen.

98b **Flowers white**.......................*Echinopsis eyriesii* **(Turpin)** *Zuccarini* is the other of two most commonly cultivated plants of this genus. The clustered heads can easily be propagated, and the long, attractive flowers make them a desirable house plant. Native to southeast South America.

99a **Flowers scarlet to salmon-colored, opening once but lasting several days** 100

99b **Flowers purple, yellow or greenish-yellow, opening in sunlight, closing at night**..104

100a Plants forming large mounds of 500-800 joints; spines white, long
   and flexuous . Fig. 103..
   ....*Echinocereus triglochidiatus* var. *mojavensis*

Figure 103

Fig. 103. *Echinocereus triglochidiatus* var. *mojavensis* (Engelmann &
Bigelow) L. Benson

Part of a mound of flowering heads × 0.5. This is a plant of the
juniper-pinyon belt of southeastern California, northwestern Arizona
to Utah.

100b Plants usually in much smaller clusters; spines brownish or gray-
   ish, not long and flexuous.................................101

101a Ribs 5-8...
   .....*Echinocereus triglochidiatus* Engelmann var. *triglochidiatus*
   The typical variety of the species is distributed through western
   Texas, New Mexico and Colorado.

Figure 104

Fig. 104. *Echinocereus triglochidiatus* var. *polyacanthus* (Engelmann) L. Benson

A single flowering joint, × 0.62.

This variant of the broad and variable species occurs in southeastern Arizona and southwestern New Mexico, mostly at 3500-5500 feet in the desert grassland and oak belt.

103a Central spines white or straw-colored..................*Echino-cereus triglochidiatus* var. *melanacanthus* (Engelmann) L. Benson
This is a variable form of the juniper-pinyon, oak and yellow pine belts at 4000-8000 feet in Arizona, southern Colorado, New Mexico and Utah. It is the Red Hedgehog Cactus known by some authors as *Echinocereus coccineus*.

103b Central spines grey to pinkish. Fig. 105......*Echinocereus rosei*

Figure 105

Fig. 105. *Echinocereus rosei* Wooton & Standley
The small, compact clumps of this plant grow in the mountains and dry hills of western Texas and southern New Mexico.

104a Flowers yellow or greenish-white..........................105

104b Flowers purple 109

105a Ribs strongly tubercled; flowers yellow......................
...............................*Echinocereus papillosus* Linke
This is a remarkable yellow-flowered species of this genus from western Texas.

Fig. 106. *Echinocereus chloranthus* (Engelmann) Rumpler

A complete flowering plant showing the fibrous roots and circular areoles, X 0.62. The plants are usually simple, as shown. The species occurs in western Texas and southeastern New Mexico. The middle position of the flowers is characteristic.

Figure 106

100

107b Areoles elliptical. Fig. 107.............*Echinocereus viridiflorus*

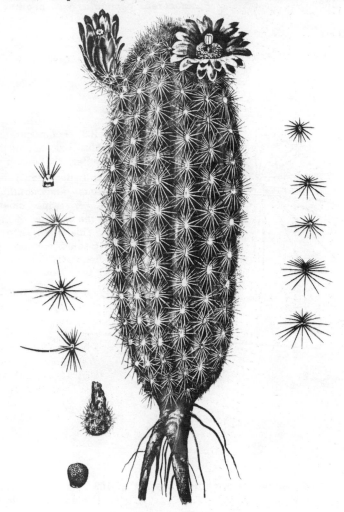

Figure 107

Fig. 107. *Echinocereus viridiflorus* Engelmann

A complete flowering plant showing elliptical areoles, various examples of spine clusters, fruit and seed, × 0.62. A common plant on the western plains, this species occurs from southern Wyoming and South Dakota to western Kansas, western Texas and eastern New Mexico. It is usually hidden in the grass because of its deeply seated nature.

101

108a Central spines in more than 1 row, or not in a vertical row. Fig.
108..................*Echinocereus pectinatus* var. *neomexicanus*

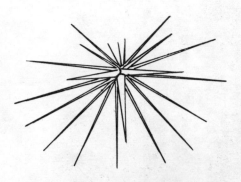

Figure 108

Fig. 108. *Echinocereus pectinatus* var. *neomexicanus* (Coulter) L. Benson

Also better known as *Echinocereus dasyacanthus* Engelm. A spine cluster to show the position of the centrals. This is the Texas Rainbow Cactus, common in the Big Bend district and westward into New Mexico.

108b Central spines in a vertical row. Fig. 109.....................
....*Echinocereus* ctenoides

109a Stems weak, slender, creeping............................110

109b Stems stout, erect or ascending............................111

Figure 109

Fig. 109. *Echinocereus ctenoides* (Engelmann) Rumpler

A flowering plant with spiraled ribs and one with straight ribs, × 0.6. Several spine clusters are enlarged to show the vertical row of centrals. This is a simple, cylindrical plant somewhat like "*E. dasyacanthus*" but of more southerly range in the south part of Texas.

110a Perianth segments narrowly oblong or linear-oblanceolate. Fig.
110 .... *Echinocereus blanckii*

Figure 110

Fig. 110. *Echinocereus blanckii* (Poselger) Palmer

A small flowering plant, × 0.9, showing the narrowly oblanceolate perianth segments. The procumbent branches of this plant form spreading clumps in southern Texas.

Figure 111

Fig. 111. *Echinocereus pentalophus* (De Candolle) Rumpler

A flowering clump in nature. This species is scattered through the southern Rio Grande Valley and along the Gulf coast of Texas. The large, brilliant flowers are spectacular. It is known as the Lady Finger Cactus.

110b Perianth segments oblong-erose. Fig. 111...................
.... *Echinocereus pentalophus*

111a Areoles elliptic; spines pectinate.........................112

111b Areoles nearly circular; spines never pectinate.............114

112a Spines of ovary and tube of flower slender and weak, the surrounding hairs long and cobwebby.......................113

112b Spines of ovary and tube of flower short and stout, the surrounding hairs short. Fig. 112.....................................
.....................*Echinocereus pectinatus* var. *rigidissimus*

Figure 112

Fig. 112. *Echinocereus pectinatus* var. *rigidissimus* (Engelmann) Engelmann. The Arizona Rainbow Cactus

Habit of a flowering plant. This species is well known in collections because of its attractive spination, color and large flowers, but its range in southernmost Arizona is small: 4000-6000 ft. in Pima, Santa Cruz and Cochise counties.

113a Spines strongly pectinate and appressed. Fig. 113..............
....................................*Echinocereus reichenbachii*

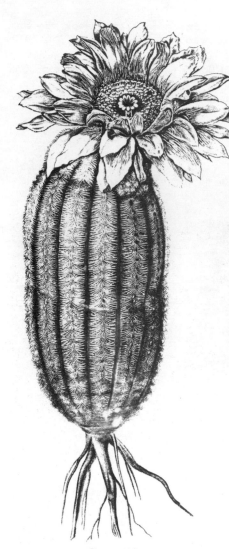

Fig. 113. *Echinocereus reich-enbachii*(Terscheck) Haage Jr.

A c o m p l e t e flowering plant, X 0.62. Known as Lace Cactus, this is one of the most widespread small cacti of Texas, growing in well-drained limestone, gran-ite and sandy areas, as far northeast as western Kansas.

Figure 113

113b Spines weakly pectinate, more or less porrect. Fig. 114........
.... *Echinocereus baileyi*

Fig. 114. *Echinocereus baileyi* Rose

A mature plant, × about 0.6. This is a species of the mountains of Oklahoma. It is common in the Wichita National Forest and may be found as solitary heads or forming clumps, sometimes of up to 25 heads.

Figure 114

114a Central spines solitary or rarely 2.........................115

114b Central spines several....................................118

115a Plants weak, becoming prostrate. Fig. 115.................
....*Echinocereus enneacanthus*

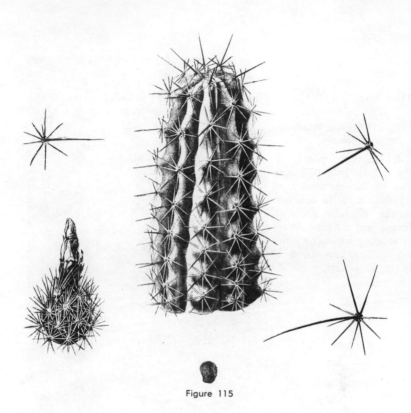

Figure 115

Fig. 115. *Echinocereus enneacanthus* Engelmann

Upper part of a joint and a maturing fruit, X 0.62. Several spine clusters and a seed, enlarged. This is a clumping species of southwestern Texas and New Mexico. There is some question about the exact scientific designation of this name, but the Strawberry Cactus of Texas has long been placed here. The juicy fruit is edible and strawberry-like when the spines are removed.

115b Plants stout, erect..116

116a Stem ribs usually 8-11, but sometimes more.................117

116b Stem ribs 13-18; principal central spine usually deflexed. Fig. 116................*Echinocereus fendleri* var. *boyce-thompsonii*

Figure 116

Fig. 116. *Echinocereus fendleri* var. *boyce-thompsonii* (Orcutt) L. Benson

A flowering plant from the home of this variety in central Arizona at elevations of 2500-5500 feet.

117a Central spine turned upward, usually curved; stems flabby. Fig.
117.........................*Echinocereus fendleri* var. *fendleri*

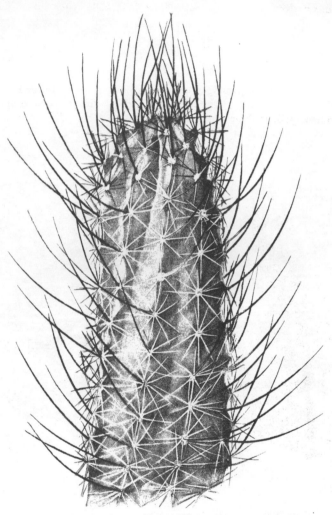

Figure 117

Fig. 117. *Echinocereus fendleri* (Engelmann) Engelmann

Upper part of a single joint, × 0.62. This is a mountain plant of grasslands and open areas at elevations of 5000-7000 feet in northern Arizona, southern Utah and northern New Mexico.

117b Central spine standing at right angles to the stem; stems rigid..
........*Echinocereus fendleri* var. *rectispinus* (Peebles) L. Benson
This is a variant from rocky slopes and benches in the desert
grassland of southern Arizona from 3500-5500 feet.

118a Spines yellowish-brown, mostly straight. Fig. 118............
.....................................*Echinocereus engelmannii*

Figure 118

Fig. 118. *Echinocereus engelmannii* (Parry) Parry
The Hedgehog Cactus of California occurs in the Mojave and
Sonora desert regions at elevations from sea level to 2500 feet. It
extends into southern Nevada and Utah, and into western Arizona.

111

118b Spines white or straw-colored, more or less twisted. Fig. 119....
.....................................*Echinocereus* stramineus

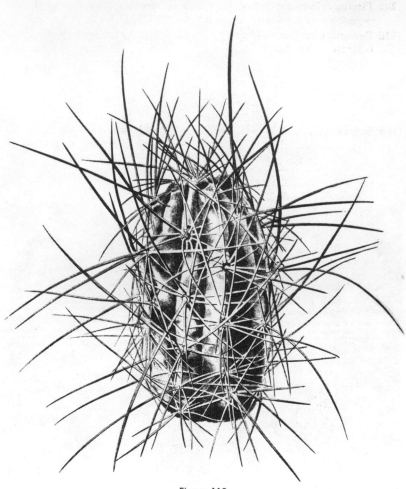

Figure 119

Fig. 119. *Echinocereus stramineus* (Engelmann) Rumpler

Upper part of a joint, × 0.62. This plant of dry mountains of western Texas and southeastern New Mexico is readily recognized by its long, curved spines densely covering the plant body.

119a Ovary and fruit naked. (See Fig. 120)......................120

119b Ovary and fruit scaly. (See Fig. 128)......................123

121a Tubercles prominent, cartilagineous, flattened, more or less imbricated. Fig. 120........................*Ariocarpus fissuratus*

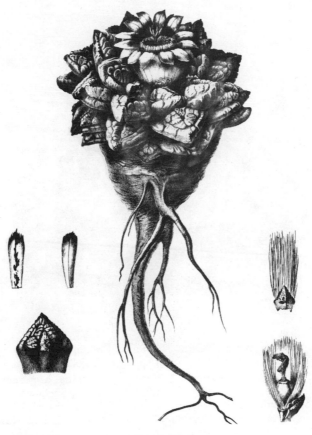

Figure 120

Fig. 120. *Ariocarpus fissuratus* (Engelmann) Schumann

The figure shows an entire flowering plant, $\times$ 0.62, and two perianth segments, an old tubercle, a young one with hairs attached and a young fruit (lower right). This is the Living Rock Cactus of the rocky hills of western Texas. It is deeply set and so well camouflaged as to be difficult to find.

121b Tubercles low, rounded above. Fig. 121....*Lophophora williamsii*

Figure 121

Fig. 121. *Lophophora williamsii* (Lemaire) Coulter

A flowering plant, × 1.25. This is the Peyote or sacred "mushroom" of the North American Indians. It contains a narcotic, and when dried slices of the plant (mescal buttons) are chewed, remarkable visions result. The plant lives in southern Texas and to central Mexico. Its possession is now regulated by the Bureau of Narcotics.

122a Fruit dry; plant globular up to 15 cm. broad. Fig. 122.........
....*Pediocactus simpsonii*

122b Fruit fleshy, indehiscent; plant 6 cm. in diameter or less, the individual heads often very small. Fig. 123....................
....*Epithelantha micromeris*

Figure 122

Fig. 122. *Pediocactus simpsonii* (Engemann) Britton & Rose

The top of a flowering plant, × 0.9. This is a widely distributed species with several striking forms, but usually easily identified. It occurs from Kansas to New Mexico north to Montana and Washington.

Figure 123

Fig. 123. *Epithelantha micromeris* (Engelmann) Weber

A cluster of our most delicately spined and smallest cactus, × 0.9. It is called Button Cactus in its western Texas home and produces small, elongated, edible fruits.

123a Flowers funnelform, the tube prominently elongated; central spine
hooked. Fig. 124 . . . .*Hamatocactus setispinus*

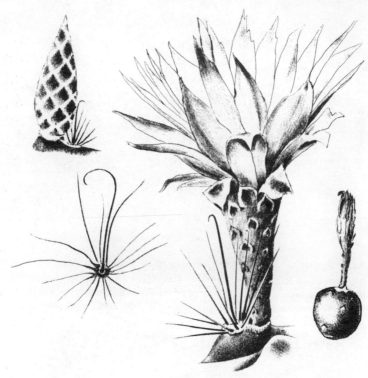

Figure 124

Fig. 124. *Hamatocactus setispinus* (Engelmann) Britton & Rose

An open flower, a bud, a spine cluster and a fruit, × 1.2. The common Fishhook Cactus of mesquite areas of southern Texas to as far
north as Austin. It flowers profusely for several months in late spring
and summer.

123b Flowers mostly campanulate, the tube short or sometimes almost
absent; central spines straight, curved or hooked 124

124a Axils of scales on ovary and fruit naked. (See Fig. 129) 125

124b Axils of scales on ovary hairy, woolly or setose 134

125a Ribs continuous, not tubercled; flowers with scarcely any tube.
(See Fig. 129) 126

125b Ribs broad, tubercled; flowers with a short but definite tube . .132

126a Plants very large, often 1 meter high or more. (See Fig. 127)..127

126b Plants much smaller, 35 cm. in diameter or less, sometimes forming small clumps...129

127a Areoles with marginal bristles. (See Fig. 126)..............128

127b Areoles without marginal bristles. Fig. 125...................
....*Ferocactus covillei*

Figure 125

Fig. 125. *Ferocactus covillei* Britton & Rose

A flowering plant in its habitat in the Organ Pipe Cactus National Monument in southern Arizona.

128a Central spine hooked. Fig. 126............*Ferocactus wizlizenii*

Figure 126

Fig. 126. *Ferocactus wizlizenii* (Engelmann) Britton & Rose.

The top of a flowering plant showing the bristle-like radial spines and hooked, flattened centrals, X 0.5. This is the commonest and largest barrel cactus of southern Arizona.

128b Central spines curved, but not hooked, spreading. Figs. 127 and 128 ....*Ferocactus acanthodes*

Fig. 127. *Ferocactus acanthodes* (Lemaire) Britton & Rose

A large example of the California Barrel Cactus in its home in the desert of southeastern California, southern Nevada and western Arizona.

Fig. 128. *Ferocactus acanthodes* (Lemaire) Britton & Rose

A medium size plant showing spination.

Figure 127

Figure 128

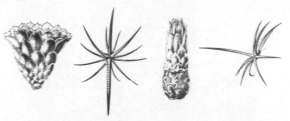

Figure 129

Fig. 129. *Ferocactus viridescens* (Torrey & Gray) Britton & Rose

Two spine clusters, an open flower and a fruit showing naked scales, × 0.62. This species of Baja California extends into our territory in the hills near the sea around San Diego, California.

130b Central spines nearly terete. Fig. 130......Ferocactus johnsonii

Figure 130

Fig. 130. *Ferocactus johnsonii* (Parry) Britton & Rose

A flowering plant. This species is fairly widespread but of only occasional occurrence in desert hills of southeastern California, southern Nevada, southwestern Utah and northwestern Arizona.

131a Flowers large, yellow; central spines 4, one of them hooked. Fig. 131............................*Ferocactus hamatacanthus*

Figure 131

Fig. 131. *Ferocactus hamatacanthus* (Muhlenpfordt) Britton & Rose
The top of a flowering plant, × 0.42. This is a north Mexico species that extends into southern Texas and New Mexico. Unlike our other ferocacti the fruit of this species is juicy and edible.

131b Flowers small, pinkish to brownish; central spine solitary, hooked ....*Ferocactus uncinatus* (Galeotti) Britton & Rose
This is the smallest of our "barrel cacti." It is usually only 10-20 cm. tall, and the hooked central spines proportionately very long. It lives in western Texas.

132a One or two of the central spines different from the others. Fig. 132a 133

Fig. 132. a. *Echinomastus intertextus* (Engelmann) Britton & Rose

A spine cluster showing four central spines, the lower one conical.

b. *Echinomastus dasyacanthus* (Engelmann) Britton & Rose

A spine cluster showing the central spines all similar to each other. This species is apparently confined to southwestern Texas.

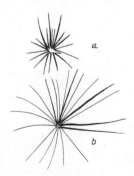

Figure 132

132b Central spines several, nearly alike. Fig. 132b..............
.....................................*Echinomastus dasyacanthus*

133a One central spine elongated, erect. (See note to Fig. 133)......
..........................*Echinomastus erectocentrus* Coulter
This is a plant of the desert grasslands of southeastern Arizona
from 3000-5000 feet.

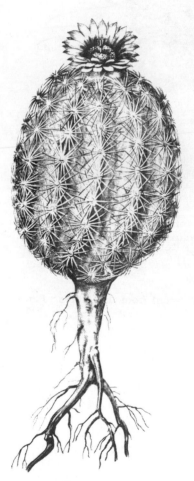

Fig. 133. *Echinomastus intertextus*
(Engelmann) Britton & Rose

An entire flowering plant, X 0.62.
This species occurs in southeastern
Arizona in the desert grasslands and
extends through southern New Mexico to western Texas. In the west it
mingles with *E. erectocentrus* and in
the east with *E. dasyacanthus*.

Figure 133

122

133b One central spine short, conical. (See Fig. 132a) Fig. 133......
.... *Echinomastus intertextus*

134a Some of the spines hooked; ovary scales few; fruit dehiscent
by a basal pore. Fig. 134...............*Sclerocactus whipplei*

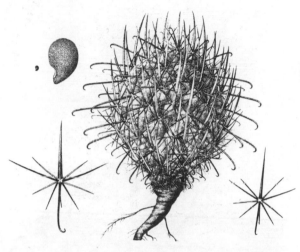

Figure 134

Fig. 134. *Sclerocactus whipplei* (Engelmann & Bigelow) Britton & Rose
An entire plant, × 0.6, together with several spine clusters and a
seed much enlarged. This is a plant of the Navajo Indian country,
occurring from northeastern Arizona and southeastern Utah up into
western Colorado. It grows on hills and plains at 5600-7000 feet.

134b Spines not hooked; ovary scales many....................135

135a Fruit permanently woolly, nearly dry, dehiscent by a terminal
pore; plants more or less globular, sometimes clustered......136

135b Fruit not so woolly, bursting irregularly, somewhat fleshy; plant usually much depressed. Fig. 135 . . . . *Homalocephala texensis*

Figure 135

Fig. 135. *Homalocephala texensis* (Hopffer) Britton & Rose

The top of a well-watered flowering plant. X 0.56. Typical specimens in nature are often more shrunken and wrinkled. The species is abundant on the high plains of western and northern Texas, extending into southeastern new Mexico. The plants are so shaped as to project very slightly above the surface level of the ground.

Figure 136

Fig. 136. *Echinocactus horizonthalonius* Lemaire

A flowering plant, × 0.6, a woolly fruit, and a seed, enlarged. This plant occurs in western Texas, southern New Mexico and in Pima County, Arizona. Its common name is Turks Head.

125

137a Seeds papillose. Fig. 137.....................................
...............*Echinocactus polycephalus* var. *polychephalus*

Figure 137

Fig. 137. Echinocactus polycephalus Engelmann & Bigelow

This is the Nigger Heads of the driest, hottest low desert mountains and valleys of eastern California and westernmost Arizona. Sometimes as many as thirty stems form a large mound.

137b Seeds smooth and shining....................................
........*Echinocactus polycephalus* var. *xeranthemoides* Coulter

This is a plant of the Grand Canyon region of northern Arizona and southern Utah at elevations of 4000-7000 feet. The young spines are not provided with the dense, short hairs as in var. *polycephalus*.

138a Flowering areoles forming a central, terminal cephalium. Fig.
138. (See also Fig. 9)...........................Cactus intortus

Figure 138

Fig. 138. Cactus intortus Miller Turk's Cap

Upper part of a fruiting plant showing the specilized fertile cephalium, X 1. This species was described in 1768 but was known since the early Spanish explorations of the West Indies. It is common in Puerto Rico and the Virgin Islands. The Turks Islands of the Lesser Antilles are named for this plant.

Figure 139

Fig. 139. *Ancistrocactus scheerii* (Salm-Dyck) Britton & Rose
Habit of a flowering plant × 0.6. This is a handsome, distinctively spined species of southern Texas, extending along the Rio Grande to nearly the Big Bend district. It has quite fleshy roots.

141b Flowers rose colored; radial spines usually 12. Fig. 140.......
..................................*Ancistrocactus brevihamatus*

Figure 140

Fig. 140. *Ancistrocactus brevihamatus* (Engelmann) Britton & Rose

An entire plant, X 0.62. This plant resembles *A. scheerii* but has the tubercles grooved all the way to the base rather than only half way. The species occurs in southern Texas from Atacosa County to the Rio Grande and west to Uvalde.

142a Tubercles not deeply grooved; fruit scaly. Fig. 141.............
.... *Thelocactus bicolor*
142b Tubercles deeply grooved; fruit nearly naked. Fig. 142........
.... *Neolloydia texensis*

Fig. 141. *Thelocactus bicolor* (Galeotti) Britton & Rose

A mature plant setting fruit. This is a species of southern Texas, occurring along the Rio Grande on the south sides of gravel hills and limestone ridges.

Figure 141

Fig. 142. *Neolloydia texensis* Britton & Rose

A rather elongated example of this species as cultivated in Arizona. As the name implies, the plant is a native of western Texas. Wild specimens may be short-oblong to nearly globular.

Figure 142

130

Fig. 143. *Coryphantha macromeris* (E n g e l - mann) Lemaire

Two tubercles showing terminal spine clusters and grooves extending only half way down, one bearing a tuft of wool, the other a bud.

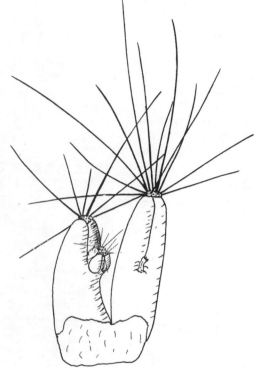

Figure 143

143a Flowers central, borne at the base of a groove on the upper side of the tubercle. (See Fig. 143)...............................144

143b Flowers lateral, borne in axils of old and mature tubercles; tubercles never grooved on the upper side...................159

144a Seeds mostly brown; fruit greenish or yellowish, even when mature, ripening slowly. *Coryphantha*......................145

144b Seeds black to dark brown; fruit red, maturing rapidly......155

145a Tubercles grooved to the middle or a little below (see Fig. 143); ovary bearing scales with woolly axils...................146

145b Tubercles grooved from tip to base except in young plants; ovary naked 147

146a Tubercles 12-30 mm. long, bright green; spines to 5 cm. long.
Figs. 143 and 144....................*Coryphantha macromeris*

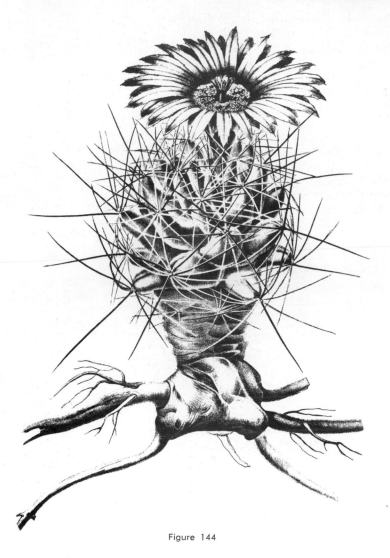

Figure 144

Fig. 144. *Coryphantha macromeris* (Engelmann) Lemaire

A flowering plant, × 0.62. This plant branches in such a way as to form a many-headed clump. It occurs in southern New Mexico and western Texas. The figure shows the fleshy character of the roots.

146b Tubercles shorter, 10-20 mm., greyish green; spines 3 cm. long
or less. Fig. 145........................*Coryphantha runyonii*

Fig. 145. *Coryphantha runyonii* Britton &
Rose

A group of tubercles, × 1, showing shorter,
more conical form and shorter spines than
C. *macromeris*. This species forms low clumps
up to 24 inches in diameter along the lower
Rio Grande Valley of Texas and adjacent
Mexico.

Figure 145

147a Flowers mostly yellowish....................................148
147b Flowers purplish, pink or salmon colored...................151
148a Spines all pectinate. Fig. 146............*Coryphantha pectinata*

Figure 146

Fig. 146. *Coryphantha pectinata* (Engelmann) Britton & Rose
A flowering plant, × 0.5, and several spine clusters. This species occurs in western and southern Texas and resembles C. *echinus*
very closely except for the presence of the prominent central spine of
the latter.

133

Fig. 147. *Coryphantha sulcata* (Engelmann) Britton & Rose

A flowering solitary specimen, somewhat reduced. Clumping examples may often occur. This is a species of rather restricted range in central southern Texas, growing on limestone hills and high sandy flats.

Figure 147

150a Long, straight central spines prominent. Fig. 148............
.... *Coryphantha echinus*

Figure 148

Fig. 148. *Coryphantha echinus* (Engelmann) Britton & Rose
A fruiting plant, a separate fruit and two spine clusters, × 0.62.
Occasional in western Texas, especially in valleys around Sanderson
and toward Fort Stockton.

150b Spines matted, the centrals not distinctive. Fig. 149............
.......................*Coryphantha deserti* (Engelmann) Britton
& Rose (*Mammillaria vivipara var. deserti* (Engelmann) L. Benson)

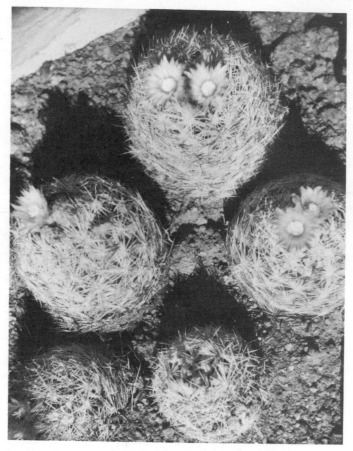

Figure 149

Fig. 149. *Coryphantha deserti* (Engelmann) Britton & Rose

This plant and the similar, greenish-flowered *Coryphantha chlorantha* are considered by Benson to be varieties of *C. vivipara*. These occur in dry Mojave Desert areas of eastern California, northwestern Arizona and southern Nevada. The brown-tipped, dense spines are distinctive.

136

HOW TO KNOW THE CACTI

151a Flowers yellowish to salmon colored..........................
...............*Coryphantha robustispina* (Schott) Britton & Rose
This is a fairly local species of southeasternmost Arizona at elevations of 2300-5000 feet. The stout, curved or hooked central spine and conspicuous truncate-conical tubercles are distinctive.
151b Flowers pink to purplish.................................152
152a Inner perianth segments linear or lanceolate..............153
152b Inner perianth segments oblanceolate........................
............*Coryphantha aggregata* (Engelmann) Britton & Rose
(*Mammillaria vivipara* var. *aggregata* (Engelmann) L. Benson)
This variety occurs in the eastern half of southern Arizona at elevations of 3000-6000 feet and on into the Gila River drainage of New Mexico. Old plants form mounds up to 2 feet in diameter, —hence, the name.
153a Stigma lobes purple, apiculate. Fig. 150.....................
...........................*Coryphantha vivipara* var. **vivipara**

Figure 150

Fig. 150. *Coryphantha vivipara* (Nuttall) Haworth var. *vivipara*
A mature, but solitary specimen, somewhat reduced. Some forms occur in mound-like clusters. The species is one of our most widely distributed small, head-like cacti, occurring from Manitoba and Alberta, Canada, south to Kansas, northern Texas and Colorado.

153b Stigma lobes white, obtuse or notched.....................154

154a Plants mostly solitary; inner perianth segments broadly linear.
Fig. 151.............................*Coryphantha neomexicana*

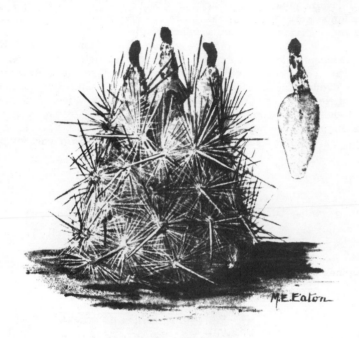

Figure 151

Fig. 151. *Coryphantha neomexicana* (Engelmann) Britton & Rose

A fruiting plant and a separate fruit, X 1.2. This is closely related
to some forms of *C. vivipara* and may not be sufficiently distinct. It
ranges through western Texas and southern New Mexico.

154b Plants mostly caespitose; inner perianth segments linear-lanceolate. Fig. 152....*Coryphantha arizonica* (Engelmann) Britton &
Rose (*Mammillaria vivipara* var. *arizonica* (Engelmann) L. Benson

155a Tubercles short, numerous, persisting after spines fall off as
woody knobs; seeds brown to black.......................156

155b Tubercles long, not numerous, not persisting as woody knobs;
seeds black, the hilum very elongate. (See Figs. 156 and 157)..158

156a Flowers large, 2.0-2.5 cm. long...........................157

156b Flowers small, about 1.5 cm. long. Fig. 153...*Escobaria runyonii*

Figure 152

Fig. 152. *Coryphantha arizonica* (Engelmann) Britton & Rose

A flowering plant, × 0.8. This is also part of the C. *vivipara* complex and is considered by some a variety of that variable species. This entity occurs in the juniper-pinyon woodland and yellow pine forests at 4000-8000 feet in northern Arizona and southern Utah.

Figure 153

Fig. 153. *Escobaria runyonii* Britton & Rose

A small clump, reduced. This species occurs in western Texas and south into Mexico. It resembles *Mammillaria multiceps* in general size, form and spination.

157a Plants elongated; seeds brown, with ventral hilum. Fig. 154....
....*Escobaria tuberculosa*

Figure 154

Fig. 154. *Escobaria tuberculosa* (Engelmann) Britton & Rose

Habit of a mature plant, × 0.62, together with an open and closed flower and two seeds (enlarged) for comparison with seeds of *Escobaria dasyacanthus* on the left at A. *E. tuberculosa* is a common species of western Texas and southern New Mexico.

157b Plants usually globose; seeds black, with subbasal hilum. Figs.
154A and 155.........................*Escobaria dasyacantha*

Figure 155

Fig. 155. *Escobaria dasyacantha* (Engelmann) Britton & Rose
A flowering plant, × 1. This plant has about the same range as
E. tuberculosa in western Texas and southern New Mexico, but its habit
and seeds are usually quite distinctive.

158a Inner perianth segments long-acuminate. Fig. 156.............
....*Neobessya similis*

Fig. 156. *Neobessya similis* (Engelmann) Britton & Rose.
A seed (× 12). This is a relatively localized species of eastern Texas.

Figure 156

Fig. 157. *Neobessya missouriensis* (Sweet) Britton & Rose.
A seed × 12. Note the elongate hilum.

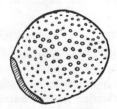

Figure 157

141

158b Inner perianth segments at most acute. Figs. 157 and 158...... .... *Neobessya missouriensis*

Figure 158

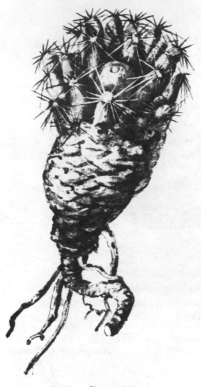

Fig. 158. *Neobessya missouriensis* (Sweet) Britton & Rose

A fruiting plant, X 1.2. This is a widely distributed species in the Great Plains region extending from North Dakota to Montana to Colorado, Kansas, Oklahoma and northern Texas. Plants may be solitary or clustered.

159a Juice of tubercles milky.................................160

159b Juice of tubercles watery, not milky........................164

160a Tubercles nearly terete toward apex........................161

160b Tubercles angled to the top. Fig. 159, 1-3.................. .... *Mammillaria meiacantha*

Fig. 159. (1-3) *Mammillaria meiacantha* Engelmann

A flowering plant is shown with a fruit and a seed. This plant inhabits western Texas and New Mexico.

(4-8) *Mammillaria applanata* Engelmann.

The top of a flowering plant is shown with separate flowers, fruit and seed. This species occurs in central and southern Texas.

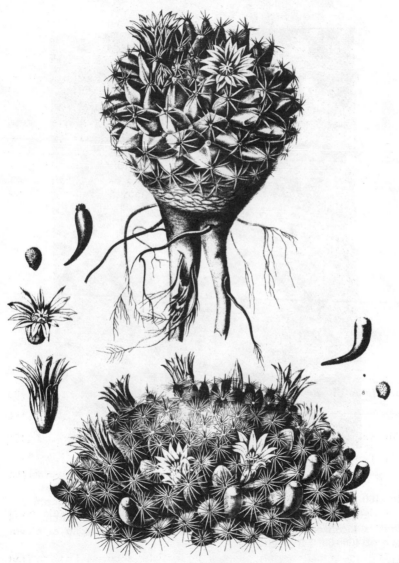

Figure 159

161a Outer perianth segments and scales more or less fimbriate; flowers light yellow. Fig. 160.....................................
.........................*Mammillaria heyderi* var. *macdougalii*

Figure 160

Fig. 160. *Mammillaria heyderi* var. *macdougalii* (Rose) L. Benson

Looking down on the top of a caespitose flowering plant. This plant is localized in the mountains of southeastern Arizona at elevations of 4000-6000 ft.

161b Outer perianth segments and scales entire.................162

162a Radial spines white; flowers pinkish. Fig. 161...............
..........................*Mammillaria heyderi* var. *heyderi*

Figure 161

Fig. 161. *Mammillaria heyderi* Muhlenpfordt var. *heyderi*

A flowering plant and fruit, × 1. This is a species of northern Mexico extending into western Texas, southern New Mexico to the southeast corner of Arizona.

162b Radial spines brownish; flowers white to cream-colored.....163

163a Plant much flattened; radial spines (10) 15-18; perianth segments acuminate. (See Fig. 159, 4-8)..........*Mammillaria applanata*

145

163b Plant hemispheric; radial spines 9-13; perianth segments acute.
Fig. 162...........................*Mammillaria hemispherica*

Figure 162

Fig. 162. *Mammillaria hemispherica* Engelmann

Looking down on a flowering plant. This is a milky-juice species of southeastern Texas. It produces abundant little red, club-shaped fruits known as "chilitos."

164a None of spines hooked......................................165

164b Some of central spines hooked.............................167

165a Radial spines weak and hair-like; flowers yellowish. Fig. 163...
...................................*Mammillaria multiceps*

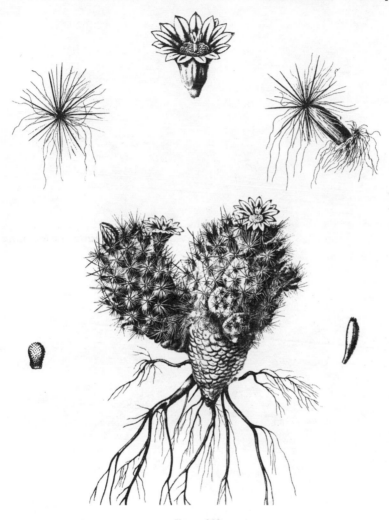

Figure 163

Fig. 163. *Mammillaria multiceps* Salm-Dyck

Habit of a complete rooted, flowering plant, × 0.62, together with enlargements of an open flower, spine-clusters showing the hair-like radials, a fruit and a seed. This is a species of the mesquite thickets of southern Texas where it it widespread but not abundant.

165b Radial spines not hair-like; flowers whitish to pinkish........166

166a Spines pubescent or puberulent. Fig. 164....................
....*Mammillaria lasiacantha*

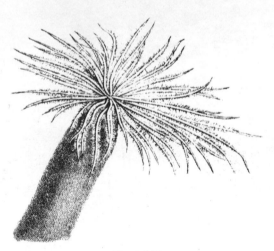

Figure 164

Fig. 164. *Mammillaria lasiacantha* Engelmann

Detail of a tubercle and a spine cluster to show the abundant fine hairs covering the spines. The dense, hairy spines give the plant a snowy white appearance. This tiny species only about an inch in diameter inhabits western Texas and is closely related to *M. denudata*.

148

166b Spines not pubescent. Fig. 165..........*Mammillaria denudata*

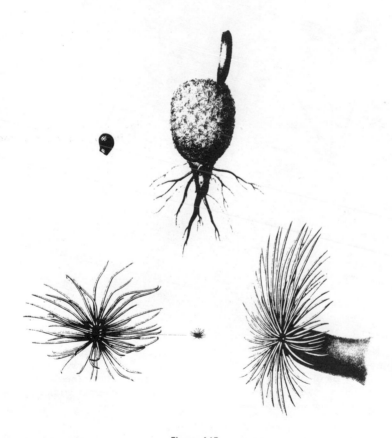

Figure 165

Fig. 165. *Mammillaria denudata* Engelmann

Habit of a fruiting plant, X 0.62, together with details of spine clusters and a seed. The plant is much like *M. lasiacantha* but lacks the hairy spines and is a little larger. It occurs in western Texas.

149

167a Base of seed corky, the corky portion half as large as the seed body; radial spines 30-60. Fig. 166.....*Mammillaria tetrancistra*

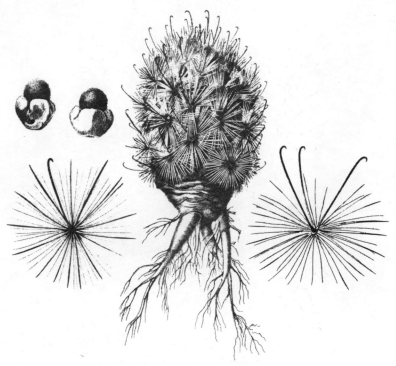

Figure 166

Fig. 166. *Mammillaria tetrancistra* Engelmann

Habit of a complete plant, X 0.62, together with enlargements of spine clusters and two seeds showing the large, corky seed-base. This is a plant of low elevations in the deserts of southeastern California and western Arizona. The very numerous slender radial spines distinguish it in the sterile condition.

167b Base of seed not corky; radial spines fewer than 30.........168

168a Outer perianth segments ciliate. Fig. 167....................
....*Mammillaria microcarpa*

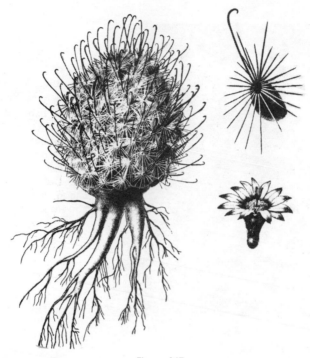

Figure 167

Fig. 167. *Mammillaria microcarpa* Engelmann

An entire plant, × 0.62, together with an open flower and a tubercle showing the spines. This is our commonest Fishhook Cactus. It is widespread and quite abundant on rocky hillsides below 5000 feet from southeastern California across to southwestern Texas.

168b Perianth segments not ciliate...............................169

169a Axils of tubercles containing setae; plants stout; flowers yellowish. Fig. 168.............................*Mammillaria dioica*

Fig. 168. *Mammillaria
dioica* K. Bandegee

This fishhook cactus
has a very different
distribution t h a n the
others, occurring in the
arid hills of southwest-
ern California in San
Diego and Imperial
counties.

Figure 168

169b Axils of tubercles without setae; plants slender, elongate; flowers
       purplish. Fig. 169.....................*Mammillaria fasciculata*

Fig. 169. *Mammillaria fasciculata* Engelmann

This is a plant of specialized habitat, usually f o u n d under shrubs in alluvial bottoms in south-central A r i z o n a. It forms clumps of over a hundred heads.

Figure 169

153

INDEX AND PICTURED-GLOSSARY

Figure 170

C

Figure 171

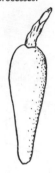

Figure 172

D

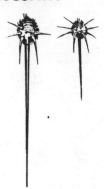

Figure 173

E

L

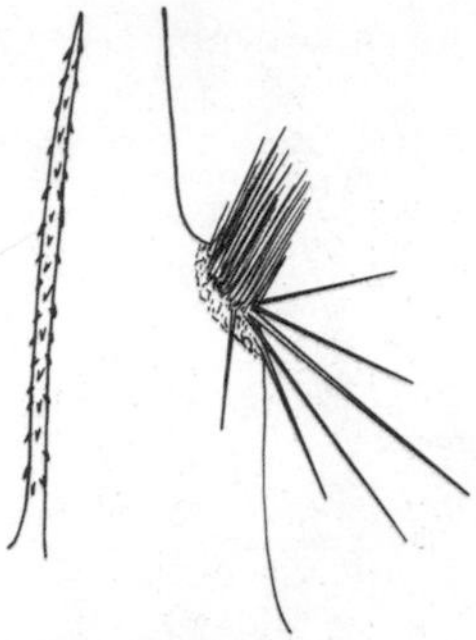

Figure 174

HILUM: the mark at the point of attachment of the ovule, showing as a basal scar on the seed. Fig. 175.
Homalocephala texensis

Figure 175

p. 124, fig. 135
Hylocereus
trigonus
p. 80, fig. 86
undatus
p. 80, fig. 85

I

IMBRICATED: overlapping, as shingles. Fig. 176.
INDEHISCENT: (fruit) not splitting or opening along any definite line.

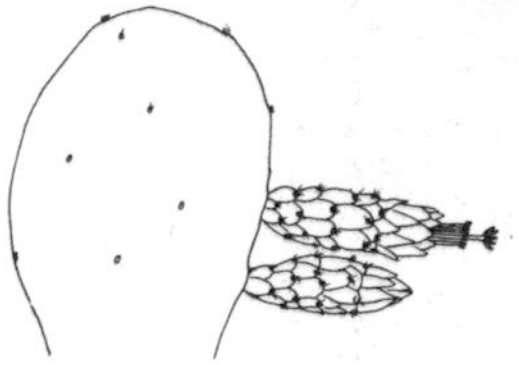

Figure 176

O

OBLANCEOLATE: shaped like
the head of a lance, but
the small end basal. Fig.
177.

Figure 177

OBOVATE: egg-shaped, but
with the small end basal.

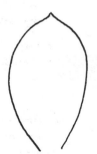

Figure 178

Opuntia
acanthocarpa
p. 31, fig. 34a
acanthocarpa var. thorn-
beri
p. 32
aciculata
p. 76, fig. 81
allairei
p. 56, fig. 60
ammophila
p. 43, fig. 46b
antillana
p. 49, fig. 52
arbuscula
p. 25, fig. 28
austrina
p. 62, fig. 67

ballii
p. 62, fig. 66
basilaris
p. 53, fig. 56
bigelovii
p. 33, fig. 36
chlorotica
p. 70, fig. 75
clavata
p. 39, fig. 42
compressa
p. 58, fig. 63, p. 61
compressa var. macrorhiza
p. 61, fig. 65
covillei
p. 68
davisii
p. 28, fig. 31
dillenii
p. 63, fig. 68, p. 72
drummondii
p. 52, fig. 55
echinocarpa
p. 30, figs. 33, 34 b-d
engelmannii
p. 69, fig. 74
erinacea var. erinacea
p. 48
erinacea var. hystricina
p. 46, fig. 49
erinacea var. ursina
p. 48, fig. 51
erinacea var. xanthostema
p. 46
ficus-indica
p. 64, fig. 69
fragilis
p. 44, fig. 47
fulgida
p. 36, figs. 32, 39
fuscoatra
p. 61
gosseliniana var. santa-
rita
p. 65, fig. 70
grahamii
p. 40, fig. 44
grandiflora
p. 58, fig. 62
imbricata
p. 35, fig. 38
juniperina
p. 45, fig. 48
kleiniae
p. 26, fig. 29
laevis
p. 71, fig. 76
leptocaulis
p. 24, fig. 27
lindheimeri
p. 74, fig. 79
linguiformis
p. 65, p. 73, fig. 78
littoralis
p. 69, p. 75, fig. 80
mackensenii
p. 61
macrarthra
p. 60, fig. 64
macrocentra
p 66, fig. 71
moniliformis
p. 43, fig. 46a
occidentalis
p. 67, 68, p. 75
opuntia
p. 58
parryi
p. 32, fig. 35

phaeacantha
p. 61, p. 68, fig. 73
pollardii
p. 57, fig 61
polyacantha
p. 47
polyacantha var. tricho-
phora
p. 47, fig. 50
pottsii
p. 55, fig. 58
prolifera
p. 38, fig. 41
pulchella
p. 40, fig. 43
ramosissima
p. 23, fig. 26
repens
p. 50, fig. 53
rufida
p. 54
schottii
p. 40
sphaerocarpa
p. 46
spinosior
p. 37, fig. 40
stanlyi var. kunzei
p. 43
stanlyi var. parishii
p. 39, fig. 42
stanlyi var. stanlyi
p. 42, fig. 45
stanlyi var. wrightiana
p. 40
stricta
p. 72, fig. 77
tardospina
p. 55, fig. 59, p. 65
tracyi
p. 53
treleasei
p. 53, fig. 57
triacantha
p. 51, fig. 54
vaseyi
p. 67, fig. 72
versicolor
p. 34, fig. 37
viridiflora
p. 29
whipplei
p. 26, fig. 30
ORBICULAR: spherical or
circular.

Figure 179

P

PAPILLOSE: covered with
small protuberances.
PECTINATE: like a comb.
Fig. 179.
Pediocactus
simpsonii
p. 114, fig. 122

Peniocereus
  greggii
    p. 88, fig 94
Pereskia
  pereskia
    p. 21, fig. 24
PERIANTH SEGMENTS: the combined petal and sepal parts of the flower.
Platyopuntia
    p. 22
PORRECT: pointing up or out. Fig. 180.

Figure 180

PROLIFEROUS: reproducing vegetatively.
PUBERULENT: minutely downy.
PUBESCENT: covered with soft, short, downy hairs.

R

Rhipsalis
  cassutha
    p. 77, fig. 82

S

SALVERFORM: trumpet-shaped; cylindrical with spreading limb.
sclerocactus
  whipplei
    p. 123, fig. 134
Selencereus
  grandiflorus
    p. 83, fig. 88
  spinulosus
    p. 83
SETACEOUS: set with bristles.
SETAE: small bristles.
SETOSE: provided with bristles.
SUBULATE: awl-shaped.

T

TERETE: cylindrical.
Thelocactus
  bicolor
    p. 130, fig. 141
Trichocereus
  spachianus
    p. 92, fig. 99
TRUNCATE: cut off.

Figure 181

TUBERCLE: an elevated part of the stem bearing an areole sometimes strongly projecting and nipple-like. Fig. 181.
TUBERCULATE: covered with tubercles. Fig. 182.
TURGID: swollen.

Figure 182

U

UNDULATE: wavy.

W

Wilcoxia
  poselgeri
    p. 89, fig. 95

Z

Zygocactus
  truncatus
    p. 78, fig. 83